THE PHYSICS
AND CHEMISTRY
OF LIFE

a
SCIENTIFIC
AMERICAN
book

SIMON AND SCHUSTER · NEW YORK

PUBLISHED BY SIMON AND SCHUSTER, INC.

ROCKEFELLER CENTER, 630 FIFTH AVENUE

NEW YORK 20, N. Y.

SIXTH PRINTING

MANUFACTURED IN THE UNITED STATES OF AMERICA

PRINTED BY MURRAY PRINTING COMPANY

LIBRARY OF CONGRESS CATALOG CARD NUMBER: 55-12531

TABLE OF CONTENTS

1. THE ORIGIN OF LIFE

As we learn more about the processes of life as they are carried on today, it becomes clear that life must have begun by spontaneous generation in the inert matter of the earth under the action of sunlight. Via the photosynthesis of starches and sugars by plants, the sun continues to provide the energy of life. The fixation of atmospheric nitrogen by certain species of bacteria supplies proteins and precursors of proteins to other living things.

2. THE MOLECULES OF LIFE

Of the 30 per cent of the substance of living things that is not water, half is protein. The primary structural materials of life, proteins are also the principal agents of its chemistry. Investigators have now established the main plan of protein structure. Even on the molecular scale, they are gratified to learn, structure is profoundly related to function.

3. THE MOLECULE OF HEREDITY

The structure of proteins goes far toward explaining how these sub-stances reproduce themselves and transmit hereditary characteristics in the cell. Viruses and rickettsiae, being scarcely more than naked nucleoproteins, provide powerful tools for investigation of this process.

4. ENZYMES AND ENERGY

One of the main functions of heredity is to equip individuals with their complement of enzymes. These are proteins that catalyze, or accelerate, the chemistry of life. The breakdown of sugar and fats by enzymes completes the energy cycle of life, converting the energy of sunlight, stored in the chemical bond, into the heat, growth and motion of living things.

5. CELL AND ORGANISM

Because a single cell can grow only to a limited size, cell division is the key process of growth. The complex apparatus that conducts this process has now been isolated from the cell. In the growth of higher organisms, the dividing cells must also differentiate into a variety of specialized tissues. Differentiation is controlled by chemicals, called organizers, still unknown.

6. MUSCLE, NERVE AND BRAIN

Muscle is a protein that converts chemical energy into mechanical energy. The basis of the activity of the nerve fiber which provides the communication system of the body is found in electrochemistry. And the activity of the brain can be read in the variation of electrical voltages.

INTRODUCTION

This book is concerned with life as a physical process. The questions raised here are the kind that can be answered wholly within the disciplines that explain the behavior of nonliving atoms and molecules. The first chapter advances an explanation of how life was originally ignited in the elements of the earth. The last chapter describes the beginning of our understanding of the electrical basis of thought. The speculations of these two authors are sustained by the work in a dozen different fields of investigation reported by the other contributors to the book. There are gaps and unknowns in the picture. But it is a connected one, and it is increasingly worthy of the attention of priests, philosophers and poets.

It is to these and other nonscientists that this book is primarily addressed. Its contents are the product of a unique collaboration between its scientist-authors and the editors of the magazine SCIENTIFIC AMERICAN, *in which the eighteen chapters were first published as articles during the past several years. Assembled in book form, each article gains in relevance from the others. Together, they present a synthesis of the state of knowledge of life that is not to be found between the covers of any other book.*

The "Origin of Life," by George Wald, is itself a synthesis of a good deal of the material in the succeeding chapters. To reconstruct the beginning of life, a scientist must marshal what we know about the processes of life as they go on today: how complex living material is built up from the simple molecules of nonliving matter; how it is endowed with the properties we associate with life; how living things reproduce themselves and transmit their characteristics to their offspring. The fact that Wald is able to account for the main issues involved in the primordial experiment is a measure of the recent vigorous progress of the life sciences.

However it began, life continues to originate on earth. Living things are constantly bringing into the processes of life the inert substances of their environment. In the great closed circle of the interdependence of life, all creatures ultimately depend upon plants. Through photosynthesis, mediated by sunlight, plants compound air and water into the elementary organic molecules of carbohydrates. The energy of sunlight, thus stored in the chemical bond, is the energy that is expended in living by the entire kingdom of life. For structural material plants and, in turn, animals depend upon hosts of obscure bacteria which have the capacity to incorporate atmospheric nitrogen into organic compounds and thus lay the foundation for the synthesis of proteins—the principal stuff of life.

The protein molecule, Joseph Fruton says, "is the noblest pieçe of architecture produced by nature." It is chiefly architecture—the infinitely various and intricate ways in which their component atoms are assembled—that gives proteins their richness and diversity in form and function. Linus Pauling and his colleagues describe the work that has now elucidated the main plan. It yields direct insight into the characteristics and behavior of the molecules as we encounter them in bone and muscle, in the bloodstream and in the nucleus of the cell. The next article describes one of the major recent triumphs of biochemistry, principally the work of Frederick Sanger of Cambridge University. This is the first complete description of a protein—the molecule of insulin—with the location of its every sub-unit and atom established.

The function of protein which perhaps has been most illuminated by this new understanding of protein structure is the central process of life: reproduction and the transmission of hereditary characteristics. Alfred Mirsky tells of the subtle work that has identified the molecule of heredity. He and other investigators have succeeded in subjecting chromosomes to chemical analysis, both in the intact cell and delicately separated from the cell. They have determined that the prime carrier of heredity is a constituent of the nucleoprotein of which the chromosome is composed. This constituent is desoxyribonucleic acid, referred to as DNA. The recent unraveling of the structure of DNA, which resembles the general plan of the protein, is described by F. H. C. Crick. From its structure, Crick shows us, we can begin to see how DNA .. endowed with the capacity to reproduce itself. We can thereby begin to account for the same capacity, in much more elaborate and complex form, in the cell. The structure of DNA also provides our first clue to the manner in which it encodes the information that determines whether the dividing cell will eventually yield a billion identical amoebas or a man.

The rich endowment of these fundamental materials of life is well demonstrated by the virus. Outside a living cell, the virus is simply an elaborate molecule of nucleoprotein. Inside a cell, as Gunther Stent shows, the virus merges itself in the chemistry and substance of its host and generates therefrom a multitude of replicas of itself. Whether viruses should be regarded as living or nonliving is a moot question. It is more interesting to ask whether they are precursors of cells or the end point of a degenerate evolution. In either case they are parasites, obliged to obtain ready-made from the cell the substances that go into their construction. For the investigator, now that virus diseases are coming under medical control, they are of interest principally as providing nucleoprotein in its handiest form.

A higher order of parasite, able to manage a somewhat broader range of life processes, is the tiny organism known as the rickettsia. It is a little bigger and more complex than a virus, but less complex than a cell. Rickettsiae are able to metabolize some substances and thus to generate a portion of their own life energy. Aside from their *interest as the agents of such diseases as typhus and Rocky Mountain spotted fever, they fascinate investigators as subjects for research into life processes.*

The comparative self-sufficiency of a rickettsia is explained by the fact that it is able to synthesize the enzymes necessary to its limited metabolism. Enzymes are the important topic of the next section of the book. These are substances, principally proteins, which act as catalysts in living systems; they speed up the otherwise slow reactions of organic molecules to the pace of life. Since each enzyme mediates but a single step in a reaction, hundreds of different ones are required to conduct any reasonably high order of existence. For example, in the metabolism of sugar, from which animals derive a major portion of their energy, no fewer than a dozen enzymes are involved. As the comparison between rickettsiae and man might suggest, the capacity to synthesize enzymes is among the characteristics transmitted by heredity. George Beadle has investigated this process in the bread mold, Neurospora. He finds that the presence or absence of a single gene will account for the presence or absence of a particular enzyme. This work strongly supports the hypothesis that the nucleoprotein material of the gene synthesizes the enzyme by some sort of replication, not unlike self-replication.

The theater for all this immense variety of biochemical activity is the microscopic living cell. Since even a virus or rickettsia depends upon the cell for reproduction, the cell may be fairly described as the irreducible unit of life. Daniel Mazia describes the still far-from-comprehended process of mitosis by which a single-celled organism divides to reproduce its kind. He and other workers have recently succeeded in isolating the mitotic apparatus and have begun the long analysis of its substance and structure. The next frontier is the question of how a single cell elaborates and differentiates into the distinct and various tissues of the multi-celled organism. C. H. Waddington reports that, while this process is held under exquisite control by organizer substances produced by the evolving organism, it is also subject to manipulation and derangement by a wide variety of common chemicals.

In the higher organisms, we come now to two vital processes which are better, if still not completely, understood. A. Szent-Györgyi tells how the elastic protein of muscle fiber converts the chemical energy yielded by sugar metabolism into the mechanical energy of action. It works like a spring in reverse: the muscle does its work when it relaxes; its contraction is the discharge of the energy it has stored. Bernhard Katz explains the ingenious electrochemistry of the nerve fiber, which provides the body with its communication system. Like a transcontinental telephone cable, it employs repeater stations, each firing the next, to conduct its messages.

The electrical activity of the brain is still an undeciphered code which scientists have just begun to read. But W. Grey Walter has been able to relate the patterns drawn by electroencephalographs and cathode-ray tubes not only to pathology but to learning, personality and emotions.

THE EDITORS *

* Board of Editors: Gerard Piel (Publisher), Dennis Flanagan (Editor), Leon Svirsky (Managing Editor), George A. W. Boehm, Robert Emmett Ginna, Jean Le Corbeiller, James R. Newman, E. P. Rosenbaum, James Grunbaum (Art Director).

PART 1 THE ORIGIN OF LIFE

I. THE ORIGIN OF LIFE *by George Wald*

One of the world's leading authorities on the chemistry of vision, George Wald is professor of biology at Harvard University. After considering careers successively in engineering, law and medicine, he found what he wanted in science—"a way of life that would always run far ahead of my capacities." It was as a graduate student at Columbia University under Selig Hecht, "a superb scientist and a great personality," that Wald developed his interest in vision, a field of research he has pursued with tenacity and increasingly rewarding discovery for some twenty years. He went to Germany on a National Research Council Fellowship, discovered Vitamin A in the retina while working in Otto Warburg's laboratory in Berlin and obtained a first view of the function of the rhodopsin cycle in rod vision in Otto Meyerhof's laboratory at Heidelberg. He received the Eli Lilly prize of the American Chemical Society in 1939 for his fundamental work in biochemistry.

II. PHOTOSYNTHESIS
by Eugene I. Rabinowitch

The community of science identifies the name of Rabinowitch with two major enterprises. The first is the subject of this chapter, on which Eugene Rabinowitch wrote the definitive treatise under the same title. Born in St. Petersburg (Leningrad) in 1901, he became a botanist after having been trained (at Berlin, Goettingen, Copenhagen, London and M. I. T.) in biochemistry and physics. This diverse background fitted him particularly for work in photosynthesis, which breaks down into a series of biochemical and physical problems. The other half—it is perhaps more than half—of his double life is occupied by the *Bulletin of the Atomic Scientists,* which Rabinowitch and his Manhattan District colleagues founded as a mimeographed newsletter in the first hours after the apocalypse of Hiroshima. Largely through his devotion and fortitude, the *Bulletin* continues publication today, reaching an increasingly numerous and influential audience, as an independent forum "for science and public affairs."

III. NITROGEN FIXATION *by Martin D. Kamen*

When Martin D. Kamen, at the age of sixteen, matriculated at the University of Chicago in 1930, he planned to concentrate in music and literature. A freshman course in chemistry, however, diverted him to the sciences, and he emerged six years later with a Ph.D. in physical chemistry. The University was then planning to build a cyclotron, and he was despatched to the University of California for training under E. O. Lawrence, inventor of the instrument. There Kamen teamed up with Samuel Ruben, a young scientist pioneering in the new field of radioactive tracer analysis in biology. Together, in 1940, they discovered Carbon 14, which has proved to be the most valuable of all the tracer isotopes. Their partnership was ended by the war, Kamen going into the Manhattan District and Ruben into the laboratories of the Chemical Warfare Service, where he lost his life in a research accident. Kamen is now associate professor at Washington University, St. Louis, where he is winning distinction as an investigator of problems in photosynthesis and metabolism.

THE ORIGIN OF LIFE

by George Wald

ABOUT a century ago the question, How did life begin? which has interested men throughout their history, reached an impasse. Up to that time two answers had been offered: one that life had been created supernaturally, the other that it arises continually from the nonliving. The first explanation lay outside science; the second was now shown to be untenable. For a time scientists felt some discomfort in having no answer at all. Then they stopped asking the question.

Recently ways have been found again to consider the origin of life as a scientific problem—as an event within the order of nature. In part this is the result of new information. But a theory never rises of itself, however rich and secure the facts. It is an act of creation. Our present ideas in this realm were first brought together in a clear and defensible argument by the Russian biochemist A. I. Oparin in a book called *The Origin of Life*, published in 1936. Much can be added now to Oparin's discussion, yet it provides the foundation upon which all of us who are interested in this subject have built.

The attempt to understand how life originated raises a wide variety of scientific questions, which lead in many and diverse directions and should end by casting light into many obscure corners. At the center of the enterprise lies the hope not only of explaining a great past event—important as that should be—but of showing that the explanation is workable. If we can indeed come to understand how a living organism arises from the nonliving, we should be able to construct one—only of the simplest description, to be sure, but still recognizably alive. This is so remote a possibility now that one scarcely dares to acknowledge it; but it is there nevertheless.

One answer to the problem of how life originated is that it was created. This is an understandable confusion of nature with technology. Men are used to making things; it is a ready thought that those things not made by men were made by a superhuman being. Most of the cultures we know contain mythical accounts of a supernatural creation of life. Our own tradition provides such an account in the opening chapters of Genesis. There we are told that beginning on the third day of the Creation, God brought forth living creatures—first plants, then fishes and birds, then land animals and finally man.

The more rational elements of society, however, tended to take a more naturalistic view of the matter. One had only to accept the evidence of one's senses to know that life arises regularly from the nonliving: worms from mud, maggots from decaying meat, mice from refuse of various kinds. This is the view that came to be called spontaneous generation. Few scientists doubted it. Aristotle, Newton, William Harvey, Descartes, van Helmont, all accepted spontaneous generation without serious question. Indeed, even the theologians—witness the English Jesuit John Turberville Needham—could subscribe to this view, for Genesis tells us, not that God created plants and most animals directly, but that He bade the earth and waters to bring them forth; since this directive was never rescinded, there is nothing heretical in believing that the process has continued.

But step by step, in a great controversy that spread over two centuries, this belief was whittled away until nothing remained of it. First the Italian Francesco Redi showed in the seventeenth century that meat placed under a screen, so that flies cannot lay their eggs on it, never develops maggots. Then in the following century the Italian abbé Lazzaro Spallanzani showed that a nutritive broth, sealed off from the air while boiling, never develops microorganisms, and hence never rots. Needham objected that by too much boiling Spallanzani had rendered the broth, and still more the air above it, incompatible with life. Spallanzani could defend his broth; when he broke the seal of his flasks, allowing new air to rush in, the broth promptly began to rot. He could find no way, however, to show that the air in the sealed flask had not been vitiated. This problem finally was solved by Louis Pasteur in 1860, with a simple modification of Spallanzani's experiment. Pasteur too used a flask containing boiling broth, but instead of sealing off the neck he drew it out in a long, S-shaped curve with its end open to the air. While molecules of air could pass back and forth freely, the heavier particles of dust, bacteria and molds in the atmosphere were trapped on the walls of the curved neck and only rarely reached the broth. In such a flask the broth seldom was contaminated; usually it remained clear and sterile indefinitely.

This was only one of Pasteur's experiments. It is no easy matter to deal with so deeply ingrained and common-sense a belief as that in spontaneous generation. One can ask for nothing better in such a pass than a noisy and stubborn opponent, and this Pasteur had in the naturalist Félix Pouchet, whose arguments before the French Academy of Sciences drove Pasteur to more and more rigorous experiments. When he had finished, nothing remained of the belief in spontaneous generation.

We tell this story to beginning students of biology as though it represents a triumph of reason over mysticism. In fact it is very nearly the opposite. The reasonable view was to believe in spontaneous generation; the only alternative, to believe in a single, primary act of supernatural creation. There is no third position. For this reason many scientists a century ago chose to regard the belief in spontaneous generation as a "philosophical necessity." It is a symptom of the philosophical poverty of our time that this necessity is no longer appreciated. Most modern biologists, having reviewed with satisfaction the downfall of the spontaneous generation hypothesis, yet unwilling to accept the alternative belief in special creation, are left with nothing.

Carbohydrates comprise one of the four principal kinds of carbon compound found in living matter. This structural formula represents part of a characteristic carbohydrate. It is a polysaccharide consisting of six-carbon sugar units, three of which are shown.

Fats are a second kind of carbon compound found in living matter. This formula represents the whole molecule of palmitin, one of the commonest fats. The molecule consists of glycerol (the 11 atoms at the far left) and fatty acids (the hydrocarbon chains at right).

6

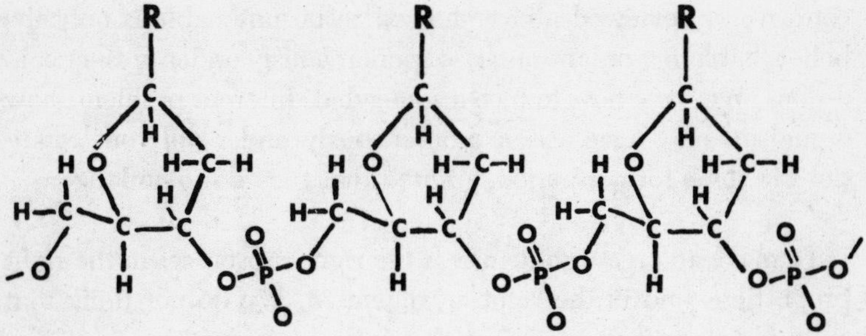

Nucleic acids are a third kind of carbon compound involved in life processes. This is part of desoxyribonucleic acid, the backbone of which is five-carbon sugars alternating with phosphoric acid. The letter R is any one of four nitrogenous bases, two purines and two pyrimidines.

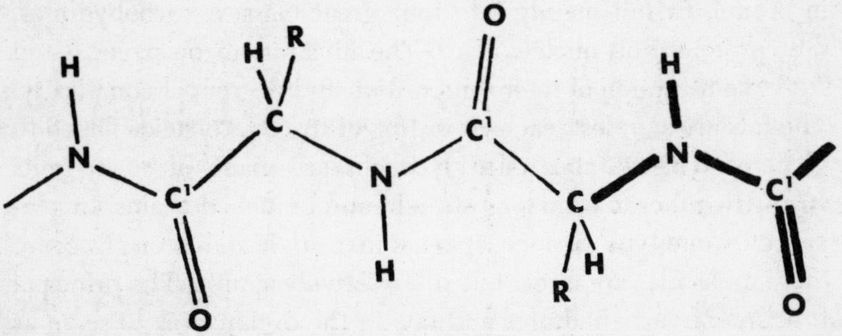

The fourth major carbon compound involved in life processes is the protein. The basic structure is the polypeptide chain shown here. The structural unit of the chain, in turn, is an amide group, isolated by the heavy lines at right. The same unit may repeat down the length of the chain, as here, or alternate with other groups.

7

I think a scientist has no choice but to approach the origin of life through a hypothesis of spontaneous generation. What the controversy reviewed above showed to be untenable is only the belief that living organisms arise spontaneously under present conditions. We have now to face a somewhat different problem: how organisms may have arisen spontaneously under different conditions in some former period, granted that they do so no longer.

To make an organism demands the right substances in the right proportions and in the right arrangement. We do not think that anything more is needed—but that is problem enough.

The substances are water, certain salts—as it happens, those found in the ocean—and carbon compounds. The latter are called *organic* compounds because they scarcely occur except as products of living organisms.

Organic compounds consist for the most part of four types of atoms: carbon, oxygen, nitrogen and hydrogen. These four atoms together constitute about 99 per cent of living material, for hydrogen and oxygen also form water. The organic compounds found in organisms fall mainly into four great classes: carbohydrates, fats, proteins and nucleic acids. The illustrations on pages 6 and 7 give some notion of their composition and degrees of complexity. The fats are simplest, each consisting of three fatty acids joined to glycerol. The starches and glycogens are made of sugar units strung together to form long straight and branched chains. In general only one type of sugar appears in a single starch or glycogen; these molecules are large, but still relatively simple. The principal function of carbohydrates and fats in the organism is to serve as fuel—as a source of energy.

The nucleic acids introduce a further level of complexity. They are very large structures, composed of aggregates of at least four types of unit—the nucleotides—brought together in a great variety of proportions and sequences. An almost endless variety of different nucleic acids is possible, and specific differences among them are believed to be of the highest importance. Indeed, these structures are thought by many to be the main constituents of the genes, the bearers of hereditary constitution.

Variety and specificity, however, are most characteristic of the proteins, which include the largest and most complex molecules known. The units of which their structure is built are about 25 different amino acids. These are strung together in chains hundreds to thousands of units long, in different proportions, in all types of sequence, and with the greatest variety of branching and folding. A virtually infinite number of different proteins is possible. Organisms seem to exploit this potentiality, for no two species of living organism, animal or plant, possess the same proteins.

Organic molecules therefore form a large and formidable array, endless in variety and of the most bewildering complexity. One cannot think of having organisms without them. This is precisely the trouble, for to understand how organisms originated we must first of all explain how such complicated molecules could come into being. And that is only the beginning. To make an organism requires not only a tremendous variety of these substances, in adequate amounts and proper proportions, but also just the right arrangement of them. Structure here is as important as composition —and what a complication of structure! The most complex machine man has devised—say an electronic brain—is child's play compared with the simplest of living organisms. The especially trying thing is that complexity here involves such small dimensions. It is on the molecular level; it consists of a detailed fitting of molecule to molecule such as no chemist can attempt.

One has only to contemplate the magnitude of this task to concede that the spontaneous generation of a living organism is impossible. Yet here we are—as a result, I believe, of spontaneous generation. It will help to digress for a moment to ask what one means by "impossible."

With every event one can associate a probability—the chance that it will occur. This is always a fraction, the proportion of times

9

the event occurs in a large number of trials. Sometimes the probability is apparent even without trial. A coin has two faces; the probability of tossing a head is therefore 1/2. A die has six faces; the probability of throwing a deuce is 1/6. When one has no means of estimating the probability beforehand, it must be determined by counting the fraction of successes in a large number of trials.

Our everyday concept of what is impossible, possible or certain derives from our experience: the number of trials that may be encompassed within the space of a human lifetime, or at most within recorded human history. In this colloquial, practical sense I concede the spontaneous origin of life to be "impossible." It is impossible as we judge events in the scale of human experience.

We shall see that this is not a very meaningful conception. For one thing, the time with which our problem is concerned is geological time, and the whole extent of human history is trivial in the balance. We shall have more to say of this later.

But even within the bounds of our own time there is a serious flaw in our judgment of what is possible. It sounds impressive to say that an event has never been observed in the whole of human history. We should tend to regard such an event as at least "practically" impossible, whatever probability is assigned to it on abstract grounds. When we look a little further into such a statement, however, it proves to be almost meaningless. For men are apt to reject reports of very improbable occurrences. Persons of good judgment think it safer to distrust the alleged observer of such an event than to believe him. The result is that events which are merely very extraordinary acquire the reputation of never having occurred at all. Thus the highly improbable is made to appear impossible.

To give an example: Every physicist knows that there is a very small probability, which is easily computed, that the table upon which I am writing will suddenly and spontaneously rise into the air. The event requires no more than that the molecules of which the table is composed, ordinarily in random motion in all direc-

THE ORIGIN OF LIFE

tions, should happen by chance to move in the same direction. Every physicist concedes this possibility; but try telling one that you have seen it happen. Recently I asked a friend, a Nobel laureate in physics, what he would say if I told him that. He laughed and said that he would regard it as more probable that I was mistaken than that the event had actually occurred.

We see therefore that it does not mean much to say that a very improbable event has never been observed. There is a conspiracy to suppress such observations, not among scientists alone, but among all judicious persons, who have learned to be skeptical even of what they see, let alone of what they are told. If one group is more skeptical than others, it is perhaps lawyers, who have the harshest experience of the unreliability of human evidence. Least skeptical of all are the scientists, who, cautious as they are, know very well what strange things are possible.

A final aspect of our problem is very important. When we consider the spontaneous origin of a living organism, this is not an event that need happen again and again. It is perhaps enough for it to happen once. The probability with which we are concerned is of a special kind; it is the probability that an event occur *at least once*. To this type of probability a fundamentally important thing happens as one increases the number of trials. However improbable the event in a single trial, it becomes increasingly probable as the trials are multiplied. Eventually the event becomes virtually inevitable. For instance, the chance that a coin will not fall head up in a single toss is 1/2. The chance that no head will appear in a series of tosses is $1/2 \times 1/2 \times 1/2$ . . . as many times over as the number of tosses. In 10 tosses the chance that no head will appear is therefore 1/2 multiplied by itself 10 times, or 1/1,000. Consequently the chance that a head will appear at least once in 10 tosses is 999/1,000. Ten trials have converted what started as a modest probability to a near certainty.

The same effect can be achieved with any probability, however small, by multiplying sufficiently the number of trials. Consider a reasonably improbable event, the chance of which is 1/1,000. The chance that this will not occur in one trial is 999/1,000. The chance that it won't occur in 1,000 trials is 999/1,000 multiplied together 1,000 times. This fraction comes out to be 37/100. The chance that it will happen at least once in 1,000 trials is therefore one minus this number—63/100—a little better than three chances out of five. One thousand trials have transformed this from a highly improbable to a highly probable event. In 10,000 trials the chance that this event will occur at least once comes out to be 19,999/20,000. It is now almost inevitable.

It makes no important change in the argument if we assess the probability that an event occur at least two, three, four or some other small number of times rather than at least once. It simply means that more trials are needed to achieve any degree of certainty we wish. Otherwise everything is the same.

In such a problem as the spontaneous origin of life we have no way of assessing probabilities beforehand, or even of deciding what we mean by a trial. The origin of a living organism is undoubtedly a stepwise phenomenon, each step with its own probability and its own conditions of trial. Of one thing we can be sure, however: whatever constitutes a trial, more such trials occur the longer the interval of time.

The important point is that since the origin of life belongs in the category of at-least-once phenomena, time is on its side. However improbable we regard this event, or any of the steps which it involves, given enough time it will almost certainly happen at least once. And for life as we know it, with its capacity for growth and reproduction, once may be enough.

Time is in fact the hero of the plot. The time with which we have to deal is of the order of two billion years. What we regard as impossible on the basis of human experience is meaningless here. Given so much time, the "impossible" becomes possible, the possible probable, and the probable virtually certain. One has only to wait: time itself performs the miracles.

This brings the argument back to its first stage: the origin of organic compounds. Until a century and a quarter ago the only known source of these substances was the stuff of living organisms. Students of chemistry are usually told that when, in 1828, Friedrich Wöhler synthesized the first organic compound, urea, he proved that organic compounds do not require living organisms to make them. Of course it showed nothing of the kind. Organic chemists are alive; Wöhler merely showed that they can make organic compounds externally as well as internally. It is still true that with almost negligible exceptions all the organic matter we know is the product of living organisms.

The almost negligible exceptions, however, are very important for our argument. It is now recognized that a constant, slow production of organic molecules occurs without the agency of living things. Certain geological phenomena yield simple organic compounds. So, for example, volcanic eruptions bring metal carbides to the surface of the earth, where they react with water vapor to yield simple compounds of carbon and hydrogen. The familiar type of such a reaction is the process used in old-style bicycle lamps in which acetylene is made by mixing iron carbide with water.

Recently Harold Urey, Nobel laureate in chemistry, has become interested in the degree to which electrical discharges in the upper atmosphere may promote the formation of organic compounds. One of his students, S. L. Miller, performed the simple experiment of circulating a mixture of water vapor, methane (CH_4), ammonia (NH_3) and hydrogen—all gases believed to have been present in the early atmosphere of the earth—continuously for a week over an electric spark. The circulation was maintained by boiling the water in one limb of the apparatus and condensing it in the other. At the end of the week the water was analyzed by the delicate method of paper chromatography. It was found to have acquired a mixture of amino acids! Glycine and alanine, the simplest amino acids and the most prevalent in proteins, were definitely identified in the solution, and there were indications it contained aspartic acid and two others. The yield was surprisingly high. This amazing result changes at a stroke our ideas of the probability of the spontaneous formation of amino acids.

A final consideration, however, seems to me more important than all the special processes to which one might appeal for organic syntheses in inanimate nature.

It has already been said that to have organic molecules one ordinarily needs organisms. The synthesis of organic substances, like almost everything else that happens in organisms, is governed by the special class of proteins called enzymes—the organic catalysts which greatly accelerate chemical reactions in the body. Since an enzyme is not used up but is returned at the end of the process, a small amount of enzyme can promote an enormous transformation of material.

Enzymes play such a dominant role in the chemistry of life that it is exceedingly difficult to imagine the synthesis of living material without their help. This poses a dilemma, for enzymes themselves are proteins, and hence among the most complex organic components of the cell. One is asking, in effect, for an apparatus which is the unique property of cells in order to form the first cell.

This is not, however, an insuperable difficulty. An enzyme, after all, is only a catalyst; it can do no more than change the *rate* of a chemical reaction. It cannot make anything happen that would not have happened, though more slowly, in its absence. Every process that is catalyzed by an enzyme, and every product of such a process, would occur without the enzyme. The only difference is one of rate.

Once again the essence of the argument is time. What takes only a few moments in the presence of an enzyme or other catalyst may take days, months or years in its absence; but given time, the end result is the same.

Indeed, this great difficulty in conceiving of the spontaneous generation of organic compounds has its positive side. In a sense,

14

organisms demonstrate to us what organic reactions and products are *possible*. We can be certain that, given time, all these things must occur. Every substance that has ever been found in an organism displays thereby the finite probability of its occurrence. Hence, given time, it should arise spontaneously. One has only to wait.

It will be objected at once that this is just what one cannot do. Everyone knows that these substances are highly perishable. Granted that, within long spaces of time, now a sugar molecule, now a fat, now even a protein might form spontaneously, each of these molecules should have only a transitory existence. How are they ever to accumulate; and, unless they do so, how form an organism?

We must turn the question around. What, in our experience, is known to destroy organic compounds? Primarily two agencies: decay and the attack of oxygen. But decay is the work of living organisms, and we are talking of a time before life existed. As for oxygen, this introduces a further and fundamental section of our argument.

It is generally conceded at present that the early atmosphere of our planet contained virtually no free oxygen. Almost all the earth's oxygen was bound in the form of water and metal oxides. It this were not so, it would be very difficult to imagine how organic matter could accumulate over the long stretches of time that alone might make possible the spontaneous origin of life. This is a crucial point, therefore, and the statement that the early atmosphere of the planet was virtually oxygen-free comes forward so opportunely as to raise a suspicion of special pleading. I have for this reason taken care to consult a number of geologists and astronomers on this point, and am relieved to find that it is well defended. I gather that there is a widespread though not universal consensus that this condition did exist. Apparently something similar was true also for another common component of our atmosphere—carbon dioxide. It is believed that most of the carbon on the earth during its early geological history existed as the element or in metal carbides and hydrocarbons; very little was combined with oxygen.

This situation is not without its irony. We tend usually to think that the environment plays the tune to which the organism must dance. The environment is given; the organism's problem is to adapt to it or die. It has become apparent lately, however, that some of the most important features of the physical environment are themselves the work of living organisms. Two such features have just been named. The atmosphere of our planet seems to have contained no oxygen until organisms placed it there by the process of plant photosynthesis. It is estimated that at present all the oxygen of our atmosphere is renewed by photosynthesis once in every 2,000 years, and that all the carbon dioxide passes through the process of photosynthesis once in every 300 years. In the scale of geological time, these intervals are very small indeed. We are left with the realization that all the oxygen and carbon dioxide of our planet are the products of living organisms, and have passed through living organisms over and over again.

In the early history of our planet, when there were no organisms or any free oxygen, organic compounds should have been stable over very long periods. This is the crucial difference between the period before life existed and our own. If one were to specify a single reason why the spontaneous generation of living organisms was possible once and is so no longer, this is the reason.

We must still reckon, however, with another destructive force which is disposed of less easily. This can be called spontaneous dissolution—the counterpart of spontaneous generation. We have noted that any process catalyzed by an enzyme can occur in time without the enzyme. The trouble is that the processes which synthesize an organic substance are reversible: any chemical reaction which an enzyme may catalyze will go backward as well as forward. We have spoken as though one has only to wait to achieve syntheses of all kinds; it is truer to say that what one achieves by waiting is *equilibria* of all kinds—equilibria in which the synthesis and dissolution of substances come into balance.

In the vast majority of the processes in which we are interested the point of equilibrium lies far over toward the side of dissolution. That is to say, spontaneous dissolution is much more probable, and hence proceeds much more rapidly, than spontaneous synthesis. For example, the spontaneous union, step by step, of amino acid units to form a protein has a certain small probability, and hence might occur over a long stretch of time. But the dissolution of the protein or of an intermediate product into its component amino acids is much more probable, and hence will go ever so much more rapidly. The situation we must face is that of patient Penelope waiting for Odysseus, yet much worse: each night she undid the weaving of the preceding day, but here a night could readily undo the work of a year or a century.

How do present-day organisms manage to synthesize organic compounds against the forces of dissolution? They do so by a continuous expenditure of energy. Indeed, living organisms commonly do better than oppose the forces of dissolution; they grow in spite of them. They do so, however, only at enormous expense to their surroundings. They need a constant supply of material and energy merely to maintain themselves, and much more of both to grow and reproduce. A living organism is an intricate machine for performing exactly this function. When, for want of fuel or through some internal failure in its mechanism, an organism stops actively synthesizing itself in opposition to the processes which continuously decompose it, it dies and rapidly disintegrates.

What we ask here is to synthesize organic molecules without such a machine. I believe this to be the most stubborn problem that confronts us—the weakest link at present in our argument. I do not think it by any means disastrous, but it calls for phenomena and forces some of which are as yet only partly understood and some probably still to be discovered.

At present we can make only a beginning with this problem.

We know that it is possible on occasion to protect molecules from dissolution by precipitation or by attachment to other molecules. A wide variety of such precipitation and "trapping" reactions is used in modern chemistry and biochemistry to promote syntheses. Some molecules appear to acquire a degree of resistance to disintegration simply through their size. So, for example, the larger molecules composed of amino acids—polypeptides and proteins— seem to display much less tendency to disintegrate into their units than do smaller compounds of two or three amino acids.

Again, many organic molecules display still another type of integrating force—a spontaneous impulse toward structure formation. Certain types of fatty molecules—lecithins and cephalins— spin themselves out in water to form highly oriented and well-shaped structures—the so-called myelin figures. Proteins sometimes orient even in solution, and also may aggregate in the solid state in highly organized formations. Such spontaneous architectonic tendencies are still largely unexplored, particularly as they may occur in complex mixtures of substances, and they involve forces the strength of which has not yet been estimated.

What we are saying is that possibilities exist for opposing *intra*molecular dissolution by *inter*molecular aggregations of various kinds. The equilibrium between union and disunion of the amino acids that make up a protein is all to the advantage of disunion, but the aggregation of the protein with itself or other molecules might swing the equilibrium in the opposite direction: perhaps by removing the protein from access to the water which would be required to disintegrate it or by providing some particularly stable type of molecular association.

In such a scheme the protein appears only as a transient intermediate, an unstable way-station, which can either fall back to a mixture of its constituent amino acids or enter into the formation of a complex structural aggregate: amino acids $\leftrightarrows$ protein $\rightarrow$ aggregate.

Such molecular aggregates, of various degrees of material and

architectural complexity, are indispensable intermediates between molecules and organisms. We have no need to try to imagine the spontaneous formation of an organism by one grand
collision of its component molecules. The whole process must be
gradual. The molecules form aggregates, small and large. The
aggregates add further molecules, thus growing in size and complexity. Aggregates of various kinds interact with one another to
form still larger and more complex structures. In this way we imagine the ascent, not by jumps or master strokes, but gradually,
piecemeal, to the first living organisms.

Where may this have happened? It is easiest to suppose that life
first arose in the sea. Here were the necessary salts and the water.
The latter is not only the principal component of organisms, but
prior to their formation provided a medium which could dissolve
molecules of the widest variety and ceaselessly mix and circulate
them. It is this constant mixture and collision of organic molecules
of every sort that constituted in large part the "trials" of our earlier
discussion of probabilities.

The sea in fact gradually turned into a dilute broth, sterile and
oxygen-free. In this broth molecules came together in increasing
number and variety, sometimes merely to collide and separate,
sometimes to react with one another to produce new combinations,
sometimes to aggregate into multimolecular formations of increasing size and complexity.

What brought order into such complexes? For order is as essential here as composition. To form an organism, molecules must
enter into intricate designs and connections; they must eventually
form a self-repairing, self-constructing dynamic machine. For a
time this problem of molecular arrangement seemed to present an
almost insuperable obstacle in the way of imagining a spontaneous
origin of life, or indeed the laboratory synthesis of a living organism. It is still a large and mysterious problem, but it no longer
seems insuperable. The change in view has come about because
we now realize that it is not altogether necessary to *bring* order

19

into this situation; a great deal of order is implicit in the molecules themselves.

The epitome of molecular order is a crystal. In a perfect crystal the molecules display complete regularity of position and orientation in all planes of space. At the other extreme are fluids—liquids or gases—in which the molecules are in ceaseless motion and in wholly random orientations and positions.

Lately it has become clear that very little of a living cell is truly fluid. Most of it consists of molecules which have taken up various degrees of orientation with regard to one another. That is, most of the cell represents various degrees of approach to crystallinity—often, however, with very important differences from the crystals most familiar to us. Much of the cell's crystallinity involves molecules which are still in solution—so-called liquid crystals—and much of the dynamic, plastic quality of cellular structure, the capacity for constant change of shape and interchange of material, derives from this condition. Our familiar crystals, furthermore, involve only one or a very few types of molecule, while in the cell a great variety of different molecules come together in some degree of regular spacing and orientation—i.e., some degree of crystallinity. We are dealing in the cell with highly mixed crystals and near-crystals, solid and liquid. The laboratory study of this type of formation has scarcely begun. Its further exploration is of the highest importance for our problem.

In a fluid such as water the molecules are in very rapid motion. Any molecules dissolved in such a medium are under a constant barrage of collisions with water molecules. This keeps small and moderately sized molecules in a constant turmoil; they are knocked about at random, colliding again and again, never holding any position or orientation for more than an instant. The larger a molecule is relative to water, the less it is disturbed by such collisions. Many protein and nucleic acid molecules are so large that even in solution their motions are very sluggish, and since they carry large numbers of electric charges distributed about their surfaces, they tend even in solution to align with respect to one another. It is so that they tend to form liquid crystals.

We have spoken above of architectonic tendencies even among some of the relatively small molecules: the lecithins and cephalins. Such molecules are insoluble in water yet possess special groups which have a high affinity for water. As a result they tend to form surface layers, in which their water-seeking groups project into the water phase, while their water-repelling portions project into the air, or into an oil phase, or unite to form an oil phase. The result is that quite spontaneously such molecules, when exposed to water, take up highly oriented positions to form surface membranes, myelin figures and other quasi-crystalline structures.

Recently several particularly striking examples have been reported of the spontaneous production of familiar types of biological structure by protein molecules. Cartilage and muscle offer some of the most intricate and regular patterns of structure to be found in organisms. A fiber from either type of tissue presents under the electron microscope a beautiful pattern of cross striations of various widths and densities, very regularly spaced. The proteins that form these structures can be coaxed into free solution and stirred into completely random orientation. Yet on precipitating, under proper conditions, the molecules realign with regard to one another to regenerate with extraordinary fidelity the original patterns of the tissues.

We have therefore a genuine basis for the view that the molecules of our oceanic broth will not only come together spontaneously to form aggregates but in doing so will spontaneously achieve various types and degrees of order. This greatly simplifies our problem. What it means is that, given the right molecules, one does not have to do everything for them; they do a great deal for themselves.

Oparin has made the ingenious suggestion that natural selection, which Darwin proposed to be the driving force of organic evolution, begins to operate at this level. He suggests that as the molecules come together to form colloidal aggregates, the latter begin to compete with one another for material. Some aggregates, by virtue of especially favorable composition or internal arrangement, acquire new molecules more rapidly than others. They eventually emerge as the dominant types. Oparin suggests further that considerations of optimal size enter at this level. A growing colloidal particle may reach a point at which it becomes unstable and breaks down into smaller particles, each of which grows and redivides. All these phenomena lie within the bounds of known processes in nonliving systems.

We suppose that all these forces and factors, and others perhaps yet to be revealed, together give us eventually the first living organism. That achieved, how does the organism continue to live?

We have already noted that a living organism is a dynamic structure. It is the site of a continuous influx and outflow of matter and energy. This is the very sign of life, its cessation the best evidence of death. What is the primal organism to use as food, and how derive the energy it needs to maintain itself and grow?

For the primal organism, generated under the conditions we have described, only one answer is possible. Having arisen in an oceanic broth of organic molecules, its only recourse is to live upon them. There is only one way of doing that in the absence of oxygen. It is called fermentation: the process by which organisms derive energy by breaking organic molecules and rearranging their parts. The most familiar example of such a process is the fermentation of sugar by yeast, which yields alcohol as one of the products. Animal cells also ferment sugar, not to alcohol but to lactic acid. These are two examples from a host of known fermentations.

The yeast fermentation has the following over-all equation: $C_6H_{12}O_6 \rightarrow 2 CO_2 + 2 C_2H_5OH + \text{energy}$. The result of fragmenting 180 grams of sugar into 88 grams of carbon dioxide and 92 grams of alcohol is to make available about 20,000 calories of energy for the use of the cell. The energy is all that the cell derives by this transaction; the carbon dioxide and alcohol are waste products which must be got rid of somehow if the cell is to survive.

The cell, having arisen in a broth of organic compounds accumulated over the ages, must consume these molecules by fermentation in order to acquire the energy it needs to live, grow and reproduce. In doing so, it and its descendants are living on borrowed time. They are consuming their heritage, just as we in our time have nearly consumed our heritage of coal and oil. Eventually such a process must come to an end, and with that life also should have ended. It would have been necessary to start the entire development again.

Fortunately, however, the waste product carbon dioxide saved this situation. This gas entered the ocean and the atmosphere in ever-increasing quantity. Some time before the cell exhausted the supply of organic molecules, it succeeded in inventing the process of photosynthesis. This enabled it, with the energy of sunlight, to make its own organic molecules: first sugar from carbon dioxide and water, then, with ammonia and nitrates as sources of nitrogen, the entire array of organic compounds which it requires. The sugar synthesis equation is: $6 \ CO_2 + 6 \ H_2O + \text{sunlight} \rightarrow C_6H_{12}O_6 + 6 \ O_2$. Here 264 grams of carbon dioxide plus 108 grams of water plus about 700,000 calories of sunlight yield 180 grams of sugar and 192 grams of oxygen.

This is an enormous step forward. Living organisms no longer needed to depend upon the accumulation of organic matter from past ages; they could make their own. With the energy of sunlight they could accomplish the fundamental organic syntheses that provide their substance, and by fermentation they could produce what energy they needed.

Fermentation, however, is an extraordinarily inefficient source of energy. It leaves most of the energy potential of organic compounds unexploited; consequently huge amounts of organic material must be fermented to provide a modicum of energy. It produces also various poisonous waste products—alcohol, lactic acid,

23

acetic acid, formic acid and so on. In the sea such products are readily washed away, but if organisms were ever to penetrate to the air and land, these products must prove a serious embarrassment.

One of the by-products of photosynthesis, however, is oxygen. Once this was available, organisms could invent a new way to acquire energy, many times as efficient as fermentation. This is the process of cold combustion called respiration: $C_6H_{12}O_6 + 6\ O_2 \rightarrow 6\ CO_2 + 6\ H_2O +$ energy. The burning of 180 grams of sugar in cellular respiration yields about 700,000 calories, as compared with the approximately 20,000 calories produced by fermentation of the same quantity of sugar. This process of combustion extracts all the energy that can possibly be derived from the molecules which it consumes. With this process at its disposal, the cell can meet its energy requirements with a minimum expenditure of substance. It is a further advantage that the products of respiration—water and carbon dioxide—are innocuous and easily disposed of in any environment.

It is difficult to overestimate the degree to which the invention of cellular respiration released the forces of living organisms. No organism that relies wholly upon fermentation has ever amounted to much. Even after the advent of photosynthesis, organisms could have led only a marginal existence. They could indeed produce their own organic materials, but only in quantities sufficient to survive. Fermentation is so profligate a way of life that photosynthesis could do little more than keep up with it. Respiration used the material of organisms with such enormously greater efficiency as for the first time to leave something over. Coupled with fermentation, photosynthesis made organisms self-sustaining; coupled with respiration, it provided a surplus. To use an economic analogy, photosynthesis brought organisms to the subsistence level; respiration provided them with capital. It is mainly this capital that they invested in the great enterprise of organic evolution.

The entry of oxygen into the atmosphere also liberated organisms in another sense. The sun's radiation contains ultraviolet components which no living cell can tolerate. We are sometimes told that if this radiation were to reach the earth's surface, life must cease. That is not quite true. Water absorbs ultraviolet radiation very effectively, and one must conclude that as long as these rays penetrated in quantity to the surface of the earth, life had to remain under water. With the appearance of oxygen, however, a layer of ozone formed high in the atmosphere and absorbed this radiation. Now organisms could for the first time emerge from the water and begin to populate the earth and air. Oxygen provided not only the means of obtaining adequate energy for evolution but the protective blanket of ozone which alone made possible terrestrial life.

This is really the end of our story. Yet not quite the end. Our entire concern in this argument has been to bring the origin of life within the compass of natural phenomena. It is of the essence of such phenomena to be repetitive, and hence, given time, to be inevitable.

This is by far our most significant conclusion—that life, as an orderly natural event on such a planet as ours, was inevitable. The same can be said of the whole of organic evolution. All of it lies within the order of nature, and apart from details all of it was inevitable.

Astronomers have reason to believe that a planet such as ours—of about the earth's size and temperature, and about as well lighted—is a rare event in the universe. Indeed, filled as our story is with improbable phenomena, one of the least probable is to have had such a body as the earth to begin with. Yet though this probability is small, the universe is so large that it is conservatively estimated at least 100,000 planets like the earth exist in our galaxy alone. Some 100 million galaxies lie within the range of our most powerful telescopes, so that throughout observable space we can count apparently on the existence of at least 10 million million planets like our own.

What it means to bring the origin of life within the realm of natural phenomena is to imply that in all these places life probably exists—life as we know it. Indeed, I am convinced that there can be no way of composing and constructing living organisms which is fundamentally different from the one we know—though this is another argument, and must await another occasion. Wherever life is possible, given time, it should arise. It should then ramify into a wide array of forms, differing in detail from those we now observe (as did earlier organisms on the earth) yet including many which should look familiar to us—perhaps even men.

We are not alone in the universe, and do not bear alone the whole burden of life and what comes of it. Life is a cosmic event —so far as we know the most complex state of organization that matter has achieved in our cosmos. It has come many times, in many places—places closed off from us by impenetrable distances, probably never to be crossed even with a signal. As men we can attempt to understand it, and even somewhat to control and guide its local manifestations. On this planet that is our home, we have every reason to wish it well. Yet should we fail, all is not lost. Our kind will try again elsewhere.

PHOTOSYNTHESIS
by Eugene I. Rabinowitch

MAN is monarch of the animal kingdom, in aggregate bulk outweighing all other animals except fishes, yet even man is less self-sufficient than the poorest weed in the field. Physiologically speaking, all the animals on land and in the sea, including man, are but a small brood of parasites living off the great body of the plant kingdom. If plants could express themselves, they would probably have the same low opinion of animals as we have of fleas and tape-worms—organisms that must lazily depend on others for survival.

We cannot conceive of life existing on the earth or any other planet without plants; our main reason for suspecting that there is life on Mars is the alleged green coloration of certain parts of that planet. So far as we know, green plants alone are able to produce the stuff of life—proteins, sugars, fats—from stable inorganic materials with no other help but the abundantly flowing light of the sun. This is the process called photosynthesis. Scientists have not been able to imitate it in the laboratory, even on a microscopic scale. But stately green trees and microscopic diatoms alike achieve it every day on a gigantic scale. Each year the plants of the earth combine about 150 billion tons of carbon with 25 billion tons of hydrogen, and set free 400 billion tons of oxygen. Few are aware, incidentally, that perhaps as much as 90 per cent of this giant chemical industry is carried on under the surface of the ocean by microscopic algae. Only 10 per cent of it is conducted on land by our familiar green plants.

A tiny fraction of the organic material synthesized by plants is later utilized as food by animals. A much larger amount is used in the respiration and other life activities of the plants themselves.

27

The greatest part, however, is decomposed into water, carbon dioxide and mineral salts by the decay of leaves and dead plants on land and in the sea. Under certain geologic or climatic conditions the decay is halted. Huge masses of half-decayed plant material then accumulate for millions of years under a protective layer of rock or silt, eventually to become peat or coal.

In endlessly repeated cycles the atoms of carbon, oxygen, and hydrogen come from the atmosphere and the hydrosphere (the world sea) into the biosphere (the thin layer of living things on the earth surface and in the upper part of the ocean). After a tour of duty which may last seconds or millions of years in the unstable organic world, they return to the stable equilibrium of inorganic nature.

The organizations of atoms in the biosphere are distinguished from those of the inorganic world by two characteristics: chemical complexity and high energy content. In the inorganic state they are simple molecules of carbon dioxide (CO_2), water (H_2O), carbonic acid (H_2CO_3), carbonate and bicarbonate ions (CO_3 $--$ and HCO_3-). In striking contrast is the complexity of even the simplest organic compounds, such as glucose ($C_6H_{12}O_6$)—not to speak of the enormous and intricate structures which are the molecules of proteins. It is this complexity that permits the almost infinite variability of organic matter. One thing, however, all the multifarious organic molecules have in common: they are all combustible, i.e., they have an affinity for oxygen. When oxidized, they release an average of about 100 kilocalories of heat for each 10 grams of carbon they contain. Thus all organic matter contains a considerable amount of "free" energy, available for conversion into mechanical motion, heat, electricity or light by gradual or sudden combination with oxygen. Such oxidations are the mainspring of life; without them, no heart could beat, no plant could grow upward defying gravity, no amoeba could swim, no sensation could speed along a nerve, no thought could flash in the human brain. Certain lower organisms can exist using sources of chemical energy not involving free oxygen, such as fermentation, but these are "exceptions that prove the rule."

Photosynthesis by plants is the process by which matter is brought up from the simplicity and inertness of the inorganic world to the complexity and reactivity that are the essence of life. The process is not only a marvel of synthetic chemical skill, but also a *tour de force* of power engineering. When plant physiologists and organic chemists study photosynthesis, they are struck most of all by the feat of manufacturing sugar from carbon dioxide and water. When physicists or photochemists contemplate the same phenomenon, they are awed and intrigued by the conversion of stable, chemically inert matter into unstable, energy-rich forms by means of visible light.

Not only are scientists unable to duplicate photosynthesis outside the living plant cell; they do not know of any halfway efficient method of converting light energy into chemical energy. If we knew the chemical secret of photosynthesis, we could perhaps bypass plants as food producers and make sugar directly from carbonates and water. If we knew its physical secret, we could p r-haps by-pass the "storage-battery" function of plants and produce chemical or electrical energy directly from sunlight. We might decompose water, for example, into an explosive mixture of hydrogen and oxygen that could be used as a source of heat or power.

The story of the little we know about photosynthesis begins with Joseph Priestley, who announced in 1772:

"I have been so happy as by accident to hit upon a method of restoring air which has been injured by the burning of candles and to have discovered at least one of the restoratives which Nature employs for this purpose. It is vegetation. One might have imagined that since common air is necessary to vegetable as well as to animal life, both plants and animals had affected it in the same manner; and I own that I had that expectation when I first put a sprig of mint into a glass jar standing inverted in a vessel of

*water; but when it had continued growing there for some months,
I found that the air would neither extinguish a candle, nor was it
at all inconvenient to a mouse which I put into it."*

In these words Priestley, religious reformer, philosopher and
spare-time naturalist of the Age of Enlightenment, described one
of the most momentous observations in the history of experimental
biology: the discovery of the capacity of plants to produce free
oxygen.

Seven years later Jan Ingen-Housz, Dutch physician to the
Austrian Empress Maria Theresa, noticed another aspect of the
same phenomenon. Ingen-Housz wrote in 1779:

*"I observed that plants not only have a faculty to correct bad
air in six or ten days by growing in it, as the experiments of Dr.
Priestley indicate, but that they perform this important office in
a complete manner in a few hours; that this wonderful operation
is by no means owing to the vegetation of the plant, but to the
influence of the light of the sun upon the plant. . . . I found that
this operation of the plants is more or less brisk in proportion to
the clearness of the day and the exposition of the plants; dimin-
ishes towards the close of the day, and ceases entirely at sunset;
that this office is not performed by the whole plant, but only by
the leaves and the green stalks. . . ."*

Thus was discovered the necessity to photosynthesis of light
and of the green pigment chlorophyll. In 1782 a Geneva pastor
named Jean Senebier added another important requirement: "fixed
air" (carbon dioxide). Only three cubic centimeters of carbon
dioxide is present in ten liters of air, but take this small amount
away and all oxygen production in light will stop.

The old and persistent theory of "humus nutrition" of plants
(even now many still believe that "good, black earth" provides
plants with organic nutrients, though in truth it supplies only inorganic minerals) had been shaken a hundred years earlier when
the Flemish physician and chemist Jan van Helmont grew a large
tree in a bucket of earth. The weight of the earth was not lessened

by an ounce. The theory was now ripe for a final overturn. The discoveries of Priestley, Ingen-Housz and Senebier, interpreted in the new chemical language of Antoine Lavoisier, indicated that green plants exposed to light absorbed carbon dioxide and liberated oxygen. An inevitable question arose: what did they do with the other constituent of carbon dioxide—carbon? In 1796 Ingen-Housz supplied the correct answer: the carbon, he said, is the basis of plant nutrition; in other words, photosynthesis is not merely "epuration of air" for the benefit of animals and man, but first of all carbon assimilation for the benefit of the plants themselves.

An important ingredient in the chemistry of photosynthesis was still missing; the omission was corrected in 1804 by another citizen of the learned city of Geneva, Nicolas Theodore de Saussure. He found that in addition to carbon dioxide, water also enters into the photosynthetic production of organic matter:

$$\text{Carbon dioxide} + \text{water} \xrightarrow[\text{light}]{\text{green plants}}$$
$$\text{organic matter} + \text{oxygen}$$

In the absence of light, or in parts of the plant that are not green, the process is reversed: respiration of the plant produces water and carbon dioxide from organic matter and oxygen.

Thus by about 1800 a general chemical definition of photosynthesis was established except for one detail—the recognition that the organic matter manufactured in photosynthesis is a carbohydrate. This class of compounds is made up of carbon combined with hydrogen and oxygen in the same ratio as in water. In the chemist's shorthand, carbohydrates may be written $C_m (H_2O)_n$. All sugars, as well as starch and cellulose, are carbohydrates. The conclusion that a compound of this type must be the first product of photosynthesis was reached by plant physiologists in about 1850, on the basis of quantitative determinations of the amounts of carbon dioxide and oxygen exchanged in photosynthesis and of qualitative observations of the formation of starch in illuminated leaves.

It was Julius Robert von Mayer, the German discoverer of the principle of conservation of energy, who first remarked the fundamental physical function of photosynthesis—the conversion of light energy into chemical energy. He wrote in 1845:

"Nature set herself the task to catch in flight the light streaming towards the earth, and to store this, the most evasive of all forces, by converting it into an immobile form. To achieve this, she has covered the earth's crust with organisms, which while living take up the sunlight and use its force to add continuously to a sum of chemical difference.

"These organisms are the plants: the plant world forms a reservoir in which the volatile sun rays are fixed and ingeniously laid down for later use; a providential economic measure, to which the very physical existence of the human race is inexorably bound."

With this perception it became clear that photosynthesis by green plants, in addition to being the only ultimate source of food on earth, also is the only source of animal energy. And indirectly, through the use of wood, coal and peat, photosynthesis is the source of most of our industrial power, heat and light; indeed of all the energy requirements of modern civilization except those met by water power and nuclear disintegrations.

Since the discoveries of Priestley, Ingen-Housz, Senebier and Mayer, hundreds of botanists, chemists and physicists have studied photosynthesis. Thousands of papers have been published on its different aspects. And yet we still do not understand photosynthesis as it occurs in the plant—a vexing situation and a continuing challenge.

The biochemist feels that he "understands" a chemical process in the living cell if he knows its successive stages, the intermediate compounds that are formed and the enzymes (biological catalysts) that make the individual stages possible. This knowledge

32

he achieves by taking the biochemical apparatus apart and putting it together again. His ultimate aim is to imitate a biochemical process, such as respiration or conversion of carbohydrates to fats, in the laboratory and to describe each step in detail by chemical equations. Our knowledge of metabolic reactions is rarely so complete, but often we know at least the main stages and can repeat them outside the living cell. We know, for example, the first steps in the breakdown of glucose by animal respiration. They are the formation of a molecule of glucose diphosphate which is then split into two molecules of a triose monophosphate; we know the enzymes involved and can repeat these reactions outside the living cell. It is true that we do not really understand the mechanism by which enzymes produce their characteristic effects, but this is a more advanced problem, the study of which comes after the elucidation of the reaction steps and identification of their enzymes.

In the case of photosynthesis, we know very little about the individual reaction steps and even less about the catalysts which make them possible. We can prepare extracts from plant cells containing chlorophyll or other pigments that are present wherever photosynthesis goes on. But not only are these extracts incapable of photosynthesis (here simply utilizing carbon dioxide and producing oxygen in light), but also we cannot find in them any catalytic or photochemical properties clearly related to the probable steps in photosynthesis. We may then decide that chemical methods of fractionating the plant-cell contents are too drastic, and attempt to take the cell apart mechanically. We take a giant green cell, such as that of some algae, and prick it with a needle in an attempt to reach its interior. Immediately photosynthesis ceases. The cell still respires, it is alive, but oxygen liberation and carbon dioxide absorption have stopped.

Thus we find ourselves in the position of being asked to find out how an automobile motor operates without being permitted to lift the hood. We see that the engine consumes carbon dioxide and water and produces an exhaust gas and chemical energy. We

33

can look at the instrument board and note how the rate of the motor's revolution depends on the supply of fuel, the temperature of the coolant and other external factors, but there is not much hope that we shall ever find out from such circumstantial evidence how the motor is constructed and what chemical reactions take place in the cylinders.

This was the situation in the study of photosynthesis until quite recently. There was no known possibility of dismantling the biochemical apparatus and studying its parts separately. It was an "all or nothing" situation: at one moment we had a living cell engaged in complete photosynthesis; at the next it was an agglomeration of broken parts or isolated chemical components, with no indications of what role, if any, they had played in photosynthesis while the cell was whole and alive.

Within the last few years the situation has changed. The problem looks less forbidding. Some progress has come from an improved general understanding of the mechanism of chemical, in particular photochemical, reactions. Some has come from the improvement of old experimental methods and the development of new ones: exact analysis by electrochemical and pressure-measuring devices, the use of radioactive tracers, quantitative spectrophotometry. None of these methods, not even the glamorous radioactive tracers, provides an immediate solution to the secrets of photosynthesis, but all of them together promise progress toward the understanding of photosynthesis *in vivo* and its imitation *in vitro*. Beyond these two achievements there beckon grandiose technological goals: synthetic production of organic materials and the unlimited supply of useful energy from sunlight without the help of plants.

From measurements of the rate of photosynthesis under different conditions, the English plant physiologist F. F. Blackman concluded as early as 1905 that photosynthesis is not a single photochemical reaction, but must include at least one "dark" reaction (one which is not affected by light). As the intensity of illumination is increased, the rate of photosynthesis (as measured, for example, by the volume of oxygen produced each minute) does not increase indefinitely but approaches a saturation state in which a further increase of light intensity has no effect. This suggests a two-stage process in which only one stage can be accelerated by light. The reasoning may be illustrated by the following analogy. If a million men are to be transported overseas in two stages—first by train to the harbor and then by ship to their destination—the provision of more and faster trains will accelerate the transportation only up to the point where all available ships are used to capacity. Thereafter the further improvement of rail transportation merely jams up the harbor. Conversely, it will serve no useful purpose to provide more ships than can be filled by the arriving trainloads. In photosynthesis there is a stage or stages accelerated by light (corresponding to the railroad journey), and another stage or stages independent of light (the ship voyage). The rate of the latter may depend on how many enzyme molecules—equivalent to ships—are available in the plant cell. It is useless to accelerate the light reaction beyond the capacity of dark reactions to transform the products of the light reaction.

The division of photosynthesis into a photochemical stage and a dark one is brought out clearly by experiments with flashing light. After a plant is exposed to a brief light flash lasting, say, for .0001 second, the liberation of oxygen continues in the dark for about .02 second; more exactly, a dark interval of about .02 second is necessary to obtain the maximum oxygen production per flash. The experiment measures directly the time required for the completion of the slowest dark reaction in photosynthesis. It is equivalent to the time our ships need to complete the ocean crossing and return to the harbor. It has also been found that there is a limit to the amount of photosynthesis that can be brought about by a single flash: the maximum yield is about one molecule of oxygen for 2,000 molecules of chlorophyll present in the cell. This is sur-

35

prising. One would expect that during a short flash each chloro-phyll molecule would have a chance to perform its function once, producing one molecule of an intermediate product. Consequently the maximum production would be one molecule of oxygen for each chlorophyll molecule, or for a small number of them. James Franck of the University of Chicago suggested an explanation of the paradox: the maximum yield per flash depends not on the number of chlorophyll molecules but on the number of molecules of the enzyme involved in the second stage (i.e., on the number of ship berths, rather than train berths). In other words, the flash can produce as many intermediate molecules as there are chloro-phyll molecules, but comparatively few of them will succeed in completing the subsequent dark stage to produce oxygen.

But why cannot the intermediates wait at the harbor while ships (the catalytic enzymes) ferry some to the other shore and return for a second, third or fourth load? Franck's explanation is that the intermediate photoproducts are unstable. Unless they are immediately processed by a "finishing" catalyst, they disap-pear by "back reactions" before the catalyst is ready for a second load (as if the soldiers, unwilling to wait, all went AWOL and drifted back to their home towns).

Thus we have the following outline of photosynthesis. It con-sists of a light stage and a dark stage. The light stage produces unstable intermediates; the dark stage stabilizes them by conver-sion into the final products, oxygen and carbohydrate. The rate of photosynthesis is limited by the bottleneck of a dark reaction which can process only one molecule, or at most a small number of molecules, of intermediates per 2,000 molecules of chlorophyll each .02 second.

From our general knowledge of the nature of chemical reactions, particularly those involved in metabolic processes, we can make a guess as to the probable nature of the light stage in photosyn-thesis. Plant respiration, the reverse of photosynthesis, involves two types of reactions: those which break the carbon chains in the large organic molecules, and those which remove hydrogen atoms from association with carbon and, with the catalytic help of enzymes, transfer them to oxygen, thus forming water. In photosynthesis the same two types of processes must be involved, but running in the opposite direction—the transfer of hydrogen from water to carbon dioxide, and the building of carbon chains. Of these two types of reactions, the transfer of hydrogen is the one that *liberates* energy in respiration, hence this must be the one that *stores* energy in photosynthesis. The energy that is stored comes from light. Consequently the light reaction in photosynthesis in all probability is a hydrogen transfer from oxygen to carbon "against the gradient of chemical potential," meaning from a more stable to a less stable form. To use a mechanical picture, in respiration the hydrogen atoms run downhill; in photosynthesis, the impact of light quanta (discrete "atoms" of light), absorbed by chlorophyll, sends them uphill.

Let us illustrate this reversible process by mixing a solution of the dyestuff thionine with a solution of ferrous sulfate. In intense light, the color of the dye disappears in a second or less; in the dark, the color immediately returns. This is an example of how an oxidation-reduction reaction can run in one direction in the dark and in the opposite direction in light. In light, ferrous iron reduces the dye to a colorless form and is itself oxidized to ferric iron; in the dark, ferric iron oxidizes the dye back to the colored form and is reduced to ferrous iron. A reaction of this type must be involved as the primary light reaction in photosynthesis, the fundamental difference being that the plant is provided with an enzymatic mechanism which efficiently prevents any back reaction in the dark—as long as the unstable light products are not supplied too fast.

The energy content of the final products of photosynthesis— sugar and oxygen—is well known; it is represented by the amount of heat produced when sugar is burned to carbon dioxide and water. The energy is 112 kilocalories per gram atom (one gram multiplied by an element's atomic weight) of carbon. This, then, is the minimum energy that has to be supplied by light in photosynthesis. To reduce (hydrogenate) a molecule of carbon dioxide to the "reduction level" of sugar, four hydrogen atoms must be transferred to the molecule:

$$CO_2 + 4H \text{-----} > C(H_2O)_2$$

To move these hydrogen atoms "uphill" from water to carbon dioxide, each of the four atoms must receive a push equivalent to at least one fourth of 112 kilocalories, or 27 kilocalories per gram atom of hydrogen. These pushes must be supplied by light.

Niels Bohr and Albert Einstein showed in 1913 that light is absorbed by atoms or molecules in the form of quanta of definite energy content, which is proportional to the wavelength of the light. Red light, which is strongly absorbed by chlorophyll, has quanta with an energy content such that it provides about 40 kilocalories per gram atom of the absorbing atoms. Obviously one such quantum is not enough to transfer four hydrogen atoms (requiring 112 kilocalories). Could it be done with four quanta—one quantum for each hydrogen atom? Even this would be a marvelous achievement: the plants would have absorbed 160 kilocalories of light energy and stored 112 kilocalories as chemical energy—an efficiency of 70 per cent.

In 1923 Otto Warburg, the German cell biologist, first attempted to measure the "quantum yield" of photosynthesis—the number of quanta required to reduce one molecule of carbon dioxide. This implied measuring exactly the light energy absorbed and the volume of oxygen produced. In order to obtain the maximum possible yield, it was advisable to work in very weak light to avoid saturation effects. The measurements therefore were very delicate. The results were striking: Warburg found an absorption of four quanta per molecule of oxygen! This corresponded with the minimum value theoretically plausible, and implied an extraordinary efficiency of plants as energy converters.

Warburg's result, however, did not remain unchallenged. Other groups of researchers were unable to confirm Warburg's observations. Instead they found yields of about 10 quanta per oxygen molecule; some values were as low as eight, but none was lower. The question is still unsettled; the weight of evidence favors the higher value: eight or more quanta per molecule of oxygen. Even at this value, however, the 35 per cent yield in energy conversion by plants is very respectable—considering that we do not know of any reaction produced by visible light *outside* the plant cell which would convert as much as 10 per cent of absorbed light into chemical energy. If some economical means could be found to capture and convert even 10 per cent of light energy, the discovery conceivably could produce a greater revolution in our power economy than can be expected at present from the much-publicized discovery of atomic energy.

One plausible picture of how chlorophyll may use eight light quanta to move four hydrogen atoms from water to carbon dioxide is this: A chlorophyll molecule absorbs a quantum and is raised to an "excited," energy-rich state. It is then able to pull a hydrogen atom away from water (or from a product derived from water by a dark, enzymatic reaction). In this reduced form, chlorophyll takes up another light quantum and uses its energy to force the same hydrogen atom on a reluctant "acceptor," such as carbon dioxide or a compound derived from carbon dioxide by a dark reaction. It is as if a workman, suspended halfway on the face of a building, fortified himself with a drink, hauled a construction piece up from the ground, and then, fortified with a second drink, threw this piece up to the roof.

It has long been assumed that chlorophyll is the only agent that can perform this trick. It has been well known that all green plants also contain yellow or orange pigments (carotenoids, identical or similar to the pigments of carrots and egg yolk), and that many algae contain red or purple pigments. But all plants capable of photosynthesis were found to contain chlorophyll, and chlorophyll

39

alone among the plant pigments absorbs red light. Since photosynthesis proceeds satisfactorily in pure red light, light absorption by chlorophyll must be *sufficient* to bring about photosynthesis, and from that experimental fact there is only a short step to the assumption that it is the *necessary* prerequisite.

Recently, however, the position of chlorophyll has been challenged. First, indications were found that the light energy absorbed by the yellow pigments also is utilized in photosynthesis. Then at the meeting of the American Association for the Advancement of Science in Chicago last December, L. R. Blinks of Stanford University presented evidence that in some red algae the light absorbed by red pigments is more effective in photosynthesis than the light absorbed by chlorophyll. If this is confirmed, the red pigments must be assumed to participate in photosynthesis directly, and not merely as handmaidens of chlorophyll. To appreciate the importance of this observation, you must remember it is estimated that 90 per cent of photosynthesis on earth is carried out, not by green land plants, but by the multicolored sea algae.

So we are beginning to get a somewhat clearer idea of the events in the light stages of photosynthesis, and recently we have also gained a little information about the dark stages. The total process, as we have noted, proceeds in two separate sequences: 1) the oxidation of water, which releases free oxygen, while hydrogen becomes attached to some intermediate "acceptor"; 2) the hydrogenation of carbon dioxide to produce carbohydrates. Each sequence of reactions apparently has a separate catalytic system. The two sequences and their relation to each other are pictured in an accompanying diagram, which shows the separate sequences as two legs, with chlorophyll as the bridge between them. One sequence (the right leg) begins with molecules of gaseous carbon dioxide. These are first bound or fixed in a form suitable for reduction, perhaps by enzymatic formation of an organic acid. The bound carbon dioxide is then reduced by hydrogen atoms supplied in light by chlorophyll, which has recovered the hydrogen from

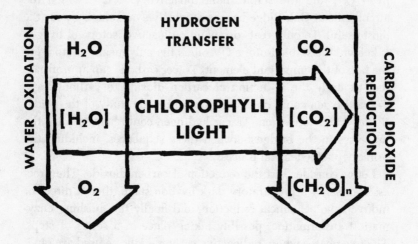

WATER OXIDATION

H_2O

HYDROGEN TRANSFER

CO_2

CARBON DIOXIDE REDUCTION

$[H_2O]$

CHLOROPHYLL LIGHT

$[CO_2]$

O_2

$[CH_2O]_n$

Photosynthesis can be visualized as an H-shaped diagram. On vertical leg at left, water gives up hydrogen, releasing oxygen. Hydrogen is then transferred to carbon dioxide by agency of light and chlorophyll. Reduction (hydrogenation) of carbon dioxide produces carbohydrate (*bottom of right leg*). Brackets indicate intermediate steps and compounds that are unresolved.

water in the other sequence. The reduction, in turn, is followed by other enzymatic transformations which lead to a carbohydrate molecule.

In the left leg we first have a similar binding of the water molecule, followed by its dehydrogenation in light, and then the enzymatic conversion of the residue into free oxygen, perhaps through the intermediate formation of a peroxide, similar to but apparently not identical with hydrogen peroxide.

Some of these reactions are now being studied with the help of isotopic tracers. We are concerned with the fate of three kinds of atoms—hydrogen, carbon, oxygen. The heavy nonradioactive hydrogen, deuterium (H^2), has been available since before the war; the weakly radioactive tritium (H^3) is not yet generally available.

41

Three isotopes of carbon are usable: the short-lived C^{11} ; the long-lived C^{14}; and the stable, nonradioactive C^{13}. C^{14}, which the atomic pile at Oak Ridge has made widely available, is by far the most useful. To our great sorrow no radioactive isotope of oxygen is known; the stable isotope O^{18} offers the only means of studying the fate of this important element. Tracer carbon is an appropriate tool to study the reduction of carbon dioxide to carbohydrate. Tracer oxygen could be equally useful for the study of the oxidation of water to oxygen. Tracer hydrogen could help to trace the processes in the bridge between these sequences, including the primary photochemical process.

Let us consider first the reduction of carbon dioxide. The process consists of a preparatory dark fixation stage, then a direct or indirect photochemical reduction, and finally the finishing enzymatic transformation, possibly taking place in a series of steps. The two phases where radioactive carbon might be used are obvious: it can be applied in the dark, with the intention of identifying the product of preliminary dark fixation, or in light, with the intention of identifying the intermediate products formed in light. Depending on the duration of exposure to light, we can expect to find the radioactive carbon distributed variously among the different intermediates and the final products of photosynthesis— sugar, starch, proteins, etc.

The first study seemed to be simpler and to provide a natural entering wedge for the tracer analysis of photosynthesis. Two groups of researchers connected with the Radiation Laboratory at the University of California have attempted it. Samuel Ruben (who died in a research accident during the war) and his co-workers used the short-lived $\bar{C}^{11}$; more recently, Melvin Calvin and co-workers used the long-lived C^{14}. The results appeared promising. It was found that radioactive CO_2 was taken up by plants in the dark. At first it seemed as if this uptake consisted in the addition of carbon dioxide without reduction to a large organic molecule, leading to the formation of an organic acid, as

42

was suggested above. In more recent experiments, however, radioactive carbon has been found in many different fractions, including partly or completely reduced ones, such as proteins or sugars. Since the amount taken up was much greater when the plants were illuminated before being exposed to radioactive carbon dioxide in the dark, Calvin suggested that the whole reduction sequence is a dark reaction; in other words, that in light chlorophyll forms some powerful, unknown reducing agent, which then reduces carbon dioxide all the way to carbohydrate without the help of light.

This hypothesis conflicts with some well-established facts. It has been observed, for example, that manometric (pressure) measurements can detect no significant carbon dioxide uptake or oxygen liberation by plants after they are deprived of light. Moreover, another possible explanation of Calvin's results has developed recently: it has been discovered that many metabolic processes in animal tissues as well as in plants involve absorption of carbon dioxide. Critics of the Calvin hypothesis have suggested that the phenomena observed at Berkeley belonged in this class, and had nothing to do with photosynthesis.

A group of workers at the University of Chicago—Hans Gaffron, A. H. Brown and E. W. Fager—have used a second approach, tracing the products formed in light, and obtained less controversial results. They studied the distribution of C^{14} in the plant after a period of illumination, and found that the shorter this period, the more pronounced was the concentration of radioactive carbon in a certain chemical fraction of the plant material—the fraction characterized by solubility in water and lack of solubility in alcohol. The striking thing about the unknown radioactive compound concentrated in this fraction was that it did not budge from the fraction even after hours of dark metabolism; on the other hand, the radioactive carbon passed rapidly into other fractions if light was again thrown on the plants. Here, then, was a true CO_2-reduction intermediate, the first such compound defi-

43

nitely pinned down in a laboratory. The next task is to isolate and identify the new compound. All researchers interested in photosynthesis are looking forward with great anticipation to the result of this tedious but very important analytical investigation.

The isotope O^{18} was employed in a study of photosynthesis by Samuel Ruben and Martin Kamen before the war, and a very significant result was obtained. Using CO_2 and H_2O containing heavy oxygen, they showed that all the oxygen liberated in photosynthesis originated in water; none came from carbon dioxide. (This is a fine example of information that only isotopic tracers can provide!) Their finding was consistent with the hypothesis that photosynthesis is fundamentally a transfer of hydrogen atoms from water to carbon dioxide, with the oxygen left behind.

Of all our recent glimpses into the mysterious mechanism of photosynthesis, none appears more promising than the one which was made possible by a discovery made in 1937 by R. Hill of Cambridge University. It had been known for a long time that dried and powdered leaves, when suspended in water and illuminated, sometimes release a small amount of oxygen, although of course they produce no carbohydrates. Hill found that the oxygen production could be increased and sustained for an hour or more if the suspension was provided with a supply of ferric oxalate or some other ferric salt. Later studies by others showed that ferric salts could be replaced by quinone or by certain dyes. All these compounds have one thing in common: they are all rather strong oxidants. They accept hydrogen atoms much more readily than carbon dioxide does. The most plausible interpretation of the results is that when leaves are dried and powdered, a product is obtained which still contains the chlorophyll bridge and the enzymatic system required to produce free oxygen (the right leg in our schematic diagram), but which has lost the left leg's enzymatic system. The suspension therefore can oxidize water and liberate oxygen in light, but it cannot reduce carbon dioxide and produce carbohydrate. Without the aid of enzymes, the carbon dioxide is

44

unable to perform its job of "accepting" hydrogen, but the reaction is kept going by substituting a more willing acceptor (e.g., ferric iron) for carbon dioxide.

Thus we have, in effect, photosynthesis without carbon dioxide! Microscopic studies yield further pertinent evidence. The photosynthesizing cells of almost all plants contain chlorophyll (and accompanying pigments) in microscopic bodies called chloroplasts. Closer observations have revealed that the pigments are further concentrated within the chloroplasts in tiny "grana," almost too small to be seen under ordinary microscopes but beautifully revealed under the electron microscope. Analysis of the Hill suspension shows that its particles are whole or broken chloroplasts or isolated grana. The grana, then, are the "bricks" in the catalytic structure of photosynthesis which permit the liberation of oxygen from water in light but do not contain the enzymes needed to take up and reduce carbon dioxide. The essential independence of the two enzymatic systems thus receives striking confirmation.

The "Hill reaction" is perhaps the widest crack that has yet appeared in the former picture of photosynthesis as a unique and indivisible process. We have lifted the hood and taken out the motor and it still runs, even though it has to be supplied with a fuel other than the usual gasoline.

It has not yet been possible to perform the converse of this feat: i.e., to eliminate the right leg of the photosynthetic apparatus and keep the left leg functioning. However, something closely related to this has been found to occur in nature: organisms capable of reducing carbon dioxide in light, but unable to use water as a reductant. As substitutes, these organisms use hydrogen sulfide, thiosulfate, or even free molecular hydrogen.

Certain species of bacteria, purple or green in color, contain a pigment called bacteriochlorophyll which is closely related to the chlorophyll of green plants. They thrive in sulfur waters or other media containing reducing agents. Cornelius B. van Niel, the

Dutch microbiologist now at Hopkins Marine Laboratory in California, has shown that they can build their organic matter from inorganic materials in light. He suggests the following general chemical equation for their photosynthesis:

$$2RH_2 + CO_2 \xrightarrow[\text{light}]{\text{bacteriochlorophyll}} C(H_2O)_2 + 2R.$$

This equation is similar to the one usually given for photosynthesis of green plants, but it is more general, since R can stand for many different radicals, consisting of a single atom or a chemically unsaturated group of atoms. If R is taken as representing an oxygen atom, we have plant photosynthesis; if it is taken to represent an atom of sulfur, we have the photosynthesis of "sulfur bacteria," and so on.

With one stroke van Niel's interpretation of the chemical activity of purple bacteria has removed photosynthesis by green plants from its entirely unique position in biological chemistry and placed it alongside other types of "photosynthetic" processes. Does this discovery indicate that the purple and green bacteria are predecessors of green plants, relics of a time when life was restricted to those places on earth where inorganic reductants were present? A time, perhaps, when the earth's crust was less well stabilized chemically than it is now, and hydrogen sulfide, sulfur, or perhaps even free hydrogen were available in much more abundance?

Further exciting vistas are opened by the similarity of the photosynthetic purple bacteria to some colorless bacteria which are capable of reducing carbon dioxide by means of the same or similar reductants but without the help of light. They use instead the chemical energy liberated by enzymatic oxidation of these reductants by the oxygen of the air. This phenomenon is called bacterial chemosynthesis; it, too, may be a relic of the more primitive forms of life. Hans Gaffron found in 1939 that if certain unicellular green algae are deprived of oxygen, they cease to be capable of ordinary photosynthesis but become capable of reducing carbon dioxide in light if hydrogen is provided as a substitute reductant to replace water! It looks as if lack of air causes these algae to simulate purple bacteria, which also can use hydrogen as reductant.

In photosynthesis, we are like travelers in an unknown country around whom the early morning fog slowly begins to rise, vaguely revealing the outlines of the landscape. It will be thrilling to see it in bright daylight!

NITROGEN FIXATION

by Martin D. Kamen

Nitrogen tantalizes mankind with the paradox of poverty in the midst of plenty. All living things on this planet—animal and vegetable—must have nitrogen in their food. The earth's atmosphere contains far more than enough nitrogen to satisfy the requirements; there are some 20 million tons of it in the air over each square mile of the earth's surface. Yet the free nitrogen in the air is so difficult to incorporate into foodstuffs that man must engage in back-breaking toil to conserve the comparatively small amount that nature captures and fixes in the soil.

To be sure, it is fortunate that nitrogen is chemically inert. If it were less reluctant to combine with other elements (and its thermodynamic relations indicate that it has the potentiality of being much more active than it ordinarily is), it might readily combine with water to form nitric acid. As some authorities on thermodynamics have pointed out, "it is to be hoped that nature will not discover a catalyst for this reaction," for if it did, the oceans would turn into dilute nitric acid—a catastrophe certainly as horrible as any visualized in speculations about atomic warfare.

Nature handles nitrogen—prodding it out of its chemical sluggishness and controlling its tendency to react rapidly thereafter—by means of a complicated cycle. Certain organisms in soil and water, called "nitrogen fixers," take up the air's free nitrogen and combine it in organic compounds which are suitable for plant or animal food. Other organisms, called "nitrifiers," convert this organic nitrogen into the mineral nitrates required by plants. Still others, the "denitrifiers," decompose dead organisms and eventually return free nitrogen to the air. Some nitrogen also is lost by washing of soil and sewage into the sea.

This continual leakage of nitrogen to the atmosphere poses one of the most important problems for the survival of living forms on the earth. Man has begun to try to stop the drain by artificial methods of recapture, but his processes for combining nitrogen with other substances are expensive and succeed only in making the simplest nitrogen compounds, such as ammonium salts, nitrates, urea and cyanamide. To make up our losses and recombine nitrogen in the forms in which plants and animals need it, we are almost entirely dependent on the nitrogen-fixing organisms.

Nature's nitrogen cycle is as important to us as the carbon cycle of photosynthesis, by which plants recapture carbon dioxide from the air and convert the carbon into organic compounds. The nitrogen fixers and the photosynthetic organisms, linked in a majestic partnership, keep the living economy of the earth solvent.

What are these natural allies of man in the struggle to wrest nitrogen from the atmosphere, and how do they do it? Obviously this is a matter of considerable importance to mankind. Unfortunately we know much less about nitrogen fixation than we do about photosynthesis, which has not yet yielded all its secrets. Within the last three years, however, there has been more progress in our knowledge of nitrogen fixers than had been made in all the previous history of research on the subject.

Until 1949 it was generally believed that very few microorganisms had the ability to fix nitrogen. The best-known were the bacteria belonging to the genus *Rhizobium,* which inhabit the root nodules of leguminous plants such as peas, barley and oats. Then there were some free-living organisms, mostly lumped in a genus called *Azotobacter,* which means simply nitrogen-fixing bacteria. There were also a few known species of nitrogen-fixing bacteria that live in the absence of oxygen, for example, species of the genus *Clostridium,* some members of which are the active agents in gas gangrene and tetanus. Finally the primitive plants called blue-green algae were known to carry out nitrogen fixation under certain conditions.

Then in 1949 and immediately afterwards came a flurry of discovery which turned up undreamed numbers of other organisms that fix nitrogen. It began with a chance finding by Howard Gest and the author during a research into a subject seemingly totally unrelated to nitrogen fixation.

We were studying the phosphate metabolism of the purple bacterium *Rhodospirillum rubrum*. Rhodospirillum is one of the many genera of photosynthetic bacteria. These bacteria, like the green plants, depend on light for growth, but instead of yielding oxygen they produce carbon dioxide and other carbon compounds as they break down organic material. We were attempting to establish the nature of the carbon compounds in which *R. rubrum* first stores the energy of light. Reasoning from analogy with what was known about processes such as muscle contraction, we deduced that certain organic phosphate compounds might be involved. In the effort to identify and locate these compounds we supplied isotopically labeled (tracer) phosphate to actively metabolizing cells of *R. rubrum* under illumination.

We found, however, that when the organisms were grown in the usual media, they produced large excess amounts of unstable phosphate which broke down during separation for chemical analysis and made it impossible to tell where the labeled phosphate had originally been taken up. We therefore had the problem of finding a diet which would allow the organisms to make only the minimum amount of phosphate required for growth. Fortunately S. H. Hutner of the Haskins Laboratories in New York had developed a completely synthetic medium for the growth of *R. rubrum* which could be adapted to our purpose simply by reduction of its phosphate content.

The dread St. Louis summer was approaching, and to make the new experiment Gest repaired to the Hopkins Marine Station at

Pacific Grove, California, where facilities had been placed at our disposal. He grew *R. rubrum* in the modified Hutner medium in glass-stoppered bottles. The source of carbon in the medium was the sodium salt of malic acid. When *R. rubrum* breaks down this malate to take carbon, it liberates the alkaline sodium and some carbon dioxide. Carbon dioxide is soluble in alkali; hence it should promptly be dissolved in the liquid. But Gest found that considerable amounts of gas were forming in the stoppered bottles: a thick froth appeared on the liquid. He quickly ascertained that the gas was hydrogen. The organisms were producing about as much hydrogen as carbon dioxide. This was altogether mystifying, for not only had the formation of hydrogen never been observed before during photosynthetic metabolism, but it was known that these bacteria possessed an active system for taking up molecular hydrogen in the presence of carbon dioxide. Although there were large amounts of carbon dioxide in the bottles, free molecular hydrogen was still being evolved.

In the autumn Gest and I tackled this mystery in our home laboratory at Washington University in St. Louis. What had begun as a routine project in phosphate nutrition had evolved quite unexpectedly into a totally different sort of research. We dropped the original inquiry in order to investigate the new phenomenon.

We soon discovered that when ammonia salts were used as a source of nitrogen for the bacteria, instead of the glutamic acid of Hutner's formula, hydrogen formation was inhibited. These observations made it easy to understand why hydrogen production had not been noted before in the many researches with cultures of *R. rubrum*. The nitrogen source customarily employed had been ammonia! Our inadvertent substitution of glutamic acid for ammonia, by adoption of Hutner's medium, had been responsible for the discovery of the ability of *R. rubrum* to produce hydrogen photochemically.

We learned that hydrogen production could be supported not only by glutamic acid but by other amino acids and a large variety

51

of carbon compounds. As a test compound for further researches we fixed on malic acid, the acid in apples. We proceeded to try to measure the production of hydrogen and carbon by the bacteria, and for these measurements we used a manometer (a device for recording pressure). The manometer vessel was filled, as is customary, with the inert gas nitrogen. We now experienced our second shock. Organisms which had been producing hydrogen quite vigorously in the usual bottle cultures stopped doing so on being transferred to the manometer vessels. At first we supposed that some contaminant in the nitrogen, probably traces of oxygen or carbon monoxide, was responsible. But after weeks of futile experimentation, involving laborious purification of the nitrogen, we concluded that no contaminating gas could account for the situation.

We finally decided to substitute other inert gases—helium and argon—for nitrogen in the manometer vessels. Now *R. rubrum* resumed producing hydrogen as before! We found further that the addition of a little nitrogen to the argon or helium promptly stopped their hydrogen production. In effect, then, molecular nitrogen appeared to be acting like ammonia with respect to the formation of hydrogen.

The fact that molecular nitrogen exerted such a profound effect on the metabolism of *R. rubrum* indicated strongly that this organism might fix nitrogen. Further experiments showed it not only might but did! This demonstration immediately generated the suspicion that many other photosynthetic bacteria might possess the same ability. It was known, for instance, that a purple sulfur bacterium belonging to the genus *Chromatium* produced hydrogen in a manner similar to that noted in *R. rubrum,* and hydrogen production appeared to be common to all photosynthetic bacteria.

At the University of Wisconsin P. W. Wilson, in collaboration with R. H. Burris and E. S. Lindstrom, soon confirmed that not only *R. rubrum* but many representative species of photosynthetic bacteria were nitrogen fixers. Nor did the matter end at this point.

From the University of Washington in Seattle Esther Duchow and H. C. Douglas sent to Wisconsin certain peculiar microbes which behaved metabolically like nonsulfur photosynthetic bacteria, though they did not resemble such bacteria. These organisms too were found to fix nitrogen.

We may pause in our chronicle at this point to remark on a fascinating historical sidelight provided in a recent article by H. Derx of the Treub Laboratory in Buitenzorg, Indonesia. Derx points out that when the Dutch bacteriologist M. W. Beijerinck discovered *Azotobacter* in 1901 he was struck by the remarkable similarities between his new organism and the photosynthetic bacterium Chromatium. Although Chromatium was not known to fix nitrogen, Beijerinck was strongly convinced that some intimate relationship between Chromatium and his new organisms would be found. We see now that his intuition was solidly based—both Azotobacter and Chromatium are nitrogen fixers. This is a good example of how the intuitions of great researchers such as Beijerinck probe deeper than they originally appear to, and of how discoveries in science rarely fail to cast a shadow before them.

The sudden emergence of nitrogen fixation in a group of organisms so widely diversified and widely distributed as photosynthetic bacteria stimulated a re-examination of the classification of bacteria. Many of the organisms classified as Azotobacter because of their nitrogen-fixing ability differ from typical Azotobacter species in appearance, in their pH requirements, in the types of cultures they form, and so on. Derx, noting the apparently widespread occurrence of the nitrogen-fixing property, argued that nitrogen fixation should not be considered an overriding criterion for bacterial classification. He proposed that on the basis of morphology and physiology some of these organisms should be classified as a new genus, for which he suggested the name *Beijerinckia*.

The number of bacteria found to be capable of nitrogen fixation steadily increases. At Wisconsin Wilson and E. D. Rosenblum studied Clostridium with sensitive tracer techniques and learned that the old contention that only a few species of this organism could fix nitrogen was untrue; of 15 species examined all but three actually do fix nitrogen. In 1951 F. D. Sisler and Claude E. ZoBell at the Scripps Institute of Oceanography in California obtained evidence of nitrogen fixation by the so-called "sulfate reducers"—organisms belonging to the genus *Desulfovibrio*. These bacteria can thrive only when oxygen is excluded from their environment. They were first isolated by Beijerinck in 1895 from canal mud and soil, and have since been found in marine sediments, in the brine of oil wells at great depths, in the water at the bottom of gasoline storage tanks and in other widely assorted places. They are often blamed for the corrosion of iron conduits, the breakdown of concrete, the destruction of large numbers of fish in the ocean and other damaging activities. These organisms make sulfide, sulfur and organic sulfur compounds as products of their metabolism. The cultures have the odor of bad eggs. Investigating the utilization of hydrogen by these organisms, Sisler and ZoBell incubated the organisms in glass-stoppered bottles of sea water with hydrogen gas in the space over the liquid. They also used a control flask with nitrogen instead of hydrogen in this space. The nitrogen disappeared from the gas phase at a rate which could not be accounted for by solution or diffusion. Growth experiments with molecular nitrogen confirmed that nitrogen fixation was taking place. Thus Desulfovibrio turned out to be not such a bad egg after all!

Probably many more nitrogen fixers remain to be discovered. The number already found presents us with a radically altered picture of potentialities in the operation of the nitrogen cycle. The root-inhabiting Rhizobia and other land organisms with which we have long been acquainted undoubtedly play a major role in maintaining the cycle, but it now appears that the oceans also may be vast reservoirs for nitrogen fixation. Possibly the organisms in the seas, including blue-green algae, fix even more nitrogen than do those in the world's soil. A great deal of nitrogen fixation may also be going on in tropical jungles, swamps and lakes. It has long been known that rice fields, for example, may remain fertile for long periods without fertilization. The Indian investigator P. K. De showed in 1938 that certain blue-green algae living in the soil of rice fields in India were very active nitrogen fixers, and concluded that they were probably the main agents in maintaining the fertility of the fields.

This classic demonstration of the importance of the blue-green algae has since been reinforced by work on the physiology and nutritional characteristics of a wide variety of them. These algae, by virtue of being both photosynthetic and nitrogen-fixing organisms, can thrive under conditions that permit no other form of life. That this is so has been shown in a number of instances. They are often the first organisms to colonize areas denuded of life, such as bare rock and soil. Within a few years after the volcanic explosion of Krakatoa in 1883, for instance, the pumice and volcanic ash had been repopulated by these dark green, gelatinous algae. Blue-green algae also are believed to contribute importantly to the production of living materials in fresh water—a fact which harasses resort operators at scenic lakes, which are often covered with profuse growths of noxious "blooms" as a result of the activities of these algae.

In hardiness and physiological versatility the photosynthetic bacteria are comparable to the algae. It may be, therefore, that the fertility of the Indian rice fields is not due solely to the algae, as De suggested, but also in part to photosynthetic bacteria.

Other potential sites of nitrogen fixation are the environments in which the sulfate-reducing organisms like to live. This is not to say that every concrete piling or iron conduit sunk in the earth becomes an inadvertent possible source of agricultural fertilization, but man may very well learn how to take useful advantage of what he learns about the capacities of these organisms.

The discovery that nitrogen can be fixed by so many more organisms than we had suspected opens up exciting vistas. We can look forward to the possibility that we may some day be able to exploit the power of these organisms, just as we have already done with Rhizobia, and so help nature's nitrogen cycle to enrich our earth.

PART 2 THE MOLECULES OF LIFE

I. PROTEINS *by Joseph S. Fruton*

Born in Poland, Joseph S. Fruton came to the U. S. as a youth, his family settling in New York City. He took his B.A. and Ph.D. degrees at Columbia University. Thereafter, for eleven years, he was a member of the staff of the Rockefeller Institute for Medical Research, where many of the exquisite techniques which he describes in this chapter were developed for the separation and analysis of protein constituents. In 1945, Fruton was appointed to the scientific faculty of Yale University, where he is now chairman of the department of biochemistry.

II. THE STRUCTURE OF PROTEINS
by Linus Pauling, Robert B. Corey and Roger Hayward

The authors of this chapter make an unusual team. Pauling, director of the Gates and Crellin Laboratories at California Institute of Technology, is one of the world's principal figures in the application of the fruitful methods and theories of modern physics to chemistry. He has made important contributions to our knowledge of chemical bonds, the structure of molecules and crystals, and immunochemistry. His work has been acknowledged by many international honors, including the Nobel prize in chemistry for 1954. He was born in Portland, Oregon, in 1901. Corey, also at Caltech, is an expert in X-ray and electron diffraction studies of crystals. Born in Springfield, Mass., in 1897, he went west to Caltech via Cornell University and the Rockefeller Institute for Medical Research. Hayward, a graduate of Massachusetts Institute of Technology, is a practicing architect in Los Angeles. An amateur in many sciences, he is an able illustrator of scientific subjects. His drawings have illuminated a number of distinguished textbooks, including *College Chemistry* by Pauling, and appear regularly in the pages of SCIENTIFIC AMERICAN. He was born in Keene, N. H., in 1899.

III. THE INSULIN MOLECULE
by E. O. P. Thompson

A biochemist with the Commonwealth Scientific and Industrial
Research Organization of Australia, E. O. P. Thompson was
graduated with first class honors in his field from Sydney University in 1945. After five years of teaching and research there,
he obtained a fellowship which enabled him to go to Cambridge
University in England to work with Frederick Sanger, whose
research on the insulin molecule he reports here. After a stop-
over in the U. S. for further work on protein structures at the
University of Utah in Salt Lake City, Thompson is now home in
Australia where he is investigating the chemistry of wool, "a
complex protein material.".

PROTEINS

by Joseph S. Fruton

There is present in plants and in animals a substance which . . . is without doubt the most important of all the known substances in living matter, and, without it, life would be impossible on our planet. This material has been named Protein.

So WROTE Gerard Johannes Mulder, a Dutch agricultural chemist, in 1838. It was in his scientific papers that the word "protein," from the Greek *proteios*, meaning of the first rank, made its first public appearance. The word had been suggested to him by the great Swedish chemist Jöns Jacob Berzelius (who also introduced to chemistry "catalysis," "polymer" and other important terms). Mulder and his great German contemporary Justus von Liebig thought that protein was a single substance—a basic structural unit existing in the same form in materials as diverse as egg white and blood fibrin. This was soon shown to be an error; the number and variety of proteins was found to be legion. But Mulder has certainly been proved correct in his emphasis on the importance of proteins to life.

The proteins are one of the three principal organic constituents of living matter (the fats and carbohydrates are the others), but in the importance and diversity of their biological functions they stand alone. They represent nearly one half of the body's dry matter. (About 70 per cent of the body is water.) Of the total body protein, more than a third is found in the muscles: the protein myosin forms the fibers that are the fundamental contractile elements in muscular movement. The bones and cartilage account

58

for another 20 per cent; here the protein collagen contributes to the structural stability of the skeleton. And the skin has about 10 per cent of the body protein, the skin protein keratin serving to protect the interior tissues against attack from the external environment.

Perhaps the most important of the proteins are the enzymes. These substances are present in only minute amounts in comparison with myosin, collagen or keratin, but they are indispensable for the promotion and direction of the body's myriad chemical reactions. They are discussed in detail later in this chapter.

Some of the hormones also are proteins. These remarkable products of the secretory activity of the endocrine organs are carried by the blood in infinitesimal amounts to the tissues, where they play a decisive role in the regulation of the pace and direction of metabolism. Still other proteins are the antibodies of the blood, which defend the organism against viruses (themselves proteins) and the harmful substances produced by disease-causing bacteria. Finally the genes, the basic units of heredity, are believed to contain a particular type of protein called nucleoproteins.

Where there is such diversity of function, there must be a corresponding diversity of chemical structure. The number of identified proteins is extremely large, and growing rapidly. To learn what proteins are present in living systems, to examine their chemical structure, to explain their biological functions in terms of their structure—these are among the most fundamental problems of modern biochemistry. When the answers to them are found, we shall have a much more precise definition of what has been termed "the physical basis of life."

To study the chemical structure of a particular protein it is necessary to destroy the cellular organization characteristic of life and to extract the protein with a suitable solvent, such as a dilute salt solution. This procedure inevitably brings into solution many of the other proteins present in the cell, and the task of separating the desired protein from the unwanted materials becomes a test of the experimenter's skill and, very frequently, of his good fortune. Proteins are extremely fragile chemical structures. This imposes serious restrictions upon the kind of laboratory procedures the chemist may use in separating them from one another. By careful control of factors such as salt concentration, alcohol concentration, acidity and temperature, fairly selective precipitation of a given protein may be achieved; today it is often possible to isolate a single protein from the dozens or even hundreds present in a tissue extract. Many individual proteins have been obtained in the form of crystals which may be recrystallized at will, thus leading to further purification. Although crystallinity *per se* is not a satisfactory criterion of a protein's purity, the availability of crystalline proteins has for the first time given to the biochemist reproducible material for the study of the chemical nature of these substances.

All proteins are made principally of carbon, hydrogen, oxygen, and nitrogen. It is the nitrogen, representing from 12 to 19 per cent of the molecule, that is the special mark of a protein. Most proteins also contain small amounts of sulfur, and many have some phosphorus. Over a century ago Mulder, noting these very small proportions of sulfur and phosphorus in his crude protein preparations, concluded that the protein molecule must be huge, since each molecule had to contain at least one atom of these elements. Proteins, in other words, are "macromolecules." Not until modern methods of measuring their molecular weights were developed, however, was it possible to determine just how large they are.

The most reliable and convenient method is to whirl them in an ultra high-speed centrifuge, a technique devised by the Swedish physical chemist, The Svedberg. The proteins are spun in a centrifuge at speeds up to 70,000 revolutions per minute, which develops a centrifugal force as much as 400,000 times that of gravity. In such a field the large protein molecules move outward from the center of rotation with selective speeds: the larger they are, the faster their motion. An ingenious optical apparatus measures the rate of this molecular sedimentation, and the molecular weight can then be calculated.

Now these measurements show that the smallest known protein is about 13,000 times as heavy as a hydrogen atom, i.e., its molecular weight is about 13,000. The largest known proteins have molecular weights of the order of 10 million. To determine the structure of molecules of such sizes is obviously quite a formidable problem. One can get some idea of how formidable it is by comparing a protein with a nonprotein organic molecule. A particularly complex example of the latter is one of the penicillins, which has a molecular weight of 334 and the formula $C_{16}H_{18}O_4N_2S$. This molecule is simplicity itself in comparison with the typical milk protein lactoglobulin, whose molecular weight is about 42,000 and whose approximate formula is $C_{1864}H_{3012}O_{576}N_{468}S_{21}$.

The structure of the penicillin molecule was worked out only after years of joint labor by the great chemists of the U. S. and England. The usual method of attacking such a task in organic chemistry is 1) to establish the proportions of the various elements in it, 2) to develop a working hypothesis about the arrangement of these atoms by a process of trial and error, and finally 3) to test the hypothesis by trying to synthesize the molecule from known substances by known chemical reactions. By this classical procedure organic chemists within the past 100 years have found the formulas of about 500,000 organic compounds, including many that are made by living organisms. But in a protein the number of atoms is so large that it has not been possible to establish its molecular structure by this method.

What the protein chemist can do at present is to cleave the protein molecule into the smaller molecules of which it is composed— the amino acids. The protein is cleaved by treatment with acids or alkalis; because water enters into the reaction, the process is called hydrolysis. When the protein has been broken down into its amino acids, the chemist can then obtain some clues to its composition, because the atomic structures of the amino acids themselves have all been determined by the classical methods of organic chemistry.

The amino acids formed by hydrolysis of a protein have certain structural features in common: each has an acidic carboxyl group (COOH) and a basic amino group (NH_2) or imino group (NH). Both the acidic and basic groups are attached to the same carbon atom, the so-called alpha-carbon. Since a carbon atom has four chemical bonds, this same alpha-carbon has two other units linked to it. One of these is invariably a hydrogen atom. What distinguishes the amino acids from one another is the fourth group attached to the alpha-carbon. This group, the so-called side chain, differs in each amino acid.

The simplest amino acid, glycine, was isolated in 1820 by the French chemist Henri Braconnot. He obtained it by acid hydrolysis of gelatine. The list of known amino acids from proteins has now grown to 22. It is not likely that many new ones will be added to it. Every protein amino acid except glycine can exist in two geometrical forms, one the mirror image of the other; by convention these are designated the "L" and "D" forms. Only the "L" type of the amino acids is obtained by the hydrolysis of proteins.

During the past 80 years an intensive effort has been devoted to the development of experimental methods for the accurate quantitative determination of the relative amounts of the various amino acids formed by hydrolysis of a protein.

Because the various amino acids are structurally similar in all respects except the nature of the side-chain group, the problem has been to find chemical processes that will select and isolate them on the basis of this rather subtle mark of identification. In the past few years this goal has been achieved, and it is now possible to say that the problem of protein analysis has been solved, at least in principle.

The most valuable contribution to the solution was the development of new chromatographic techniques for the separation of amino acids. Chromatography itself was invented by the Russian botanist Michael Tswett in 1906. It got its name from the fact that it was first used to separate pigments. Tswett was interested in isolating the chlorophyll pigments of green leaves. He conceived the idea that they might be separated quickly by taking advantage of their differing rates of adsorption by an adsorbing material. As he himself described it, "if a petroleum ether solution of chlorophyll is filtered through a column of an adsorbent (I use mainly calcium carbonate which is stamped firmly into a narrow glass tube), then the pigments . . . are resolved from top to bottom into various colored zones, since the more strongly absorbed pigments displace the more weakly absorbed ones and force them farther downwards. This separation becomes practically complete if, after the pigment solution has flowed through, one passes a stream of pure solvent through the adsorbent column. Like light rays in the spectrum, so the different components of a pigment mixture are resolved on the calcium carbonate column . . . and can be estimated on it qualitatively and quantitatively. Such a preparation I term a chromatogram and the corresponding method, the chromatographic method."

Tswett realized that "the adsorption phenomena described are not restricted to the chlorophyll pigments, and one must assume that all kinds of colored and colorless chemical compounds are subject to the same laws." It was many years before this brilliant intuition of Tswett was appreciated. Since 1930 chromatographic techniques have been developed to separate colorless as well as colored chemical compounds. It was the English chemists A. J. P. Martin and R. L. M. Synge who found a way to apply the technique to the separation of amino acids. They introduced the use of a starch column as the adsorbent. From this idea William H. Stein and Stanford Moore of the Rockefeller Institute for Medical Research later worked out a beautiful method for the precise quantitative analysis of all the amino acids formed when a protein is hydrolyzed.

So far only a few proteins have been studied by this method, but

63

the results attained are sufficient to indicate its great importance in protein chemistry. Nevertheless, it has not by any means solved the problem of protein structure. What this advance has accomplished is to bring the proteins to the historical stage reached by the simpler organic molecules a century ago, when it became possible to calculate the relative proportions of the atoms constituting an organic compound. From this, organic chemists were able to go on to discover the arrangement of the atoms in an organic molecule. In the same way protein chemists are now in a position to proceed with greater confidence to consider the spatial arrangement of amino acids in a protein molecule.

The next question concerns the nature of the linkages between the individual amino acids. The most widely accepted hypothesis is one proposed independently by Emil Fischer and the German biochemist Franz Hofmeister in 1902. They suggested that the amino group attached to the alpha-carbon of one amino acid is joined to the carboxyl group attached to the alpha-carbon of another. This union is accompanied by the elimination of the elements of water from the molecules that unite. It is this bond that is broken when the elements of water are introduced in acid hydrolysis. The bond is called a "peptide linkage," and the Fischer-Hofmeister hypothesis is known as the peptide theory.

The theory has been supported by so much experimental evidence that its essential truth seems highly probable. Support for the theory came from work on artificially synthesized peptides, i.e., groups of amino acids linked together by peptide bonds. In this Fischer was the pioneer; he pointed out that "if one wishes to attain clear results in this difficult field, one must first discover a method which will permit the experimenter to join the various amino acids to one another in a stepwise manner and with well-defined intermediary products." Much research has been done during the past half-century, and is still continuing, to develop methods for the laboratory synthesis of peptides. One of the greatest achievements came in 1932 with the invention of the "carbobenzoxy" method by a distinguished pupil of Fischer, Max Bergmann, who was then director of the Kaiser Wilhelm Institute for Leather Research in Dresden and later came to the Rockefeller Institute for Medical Research.

In living systems proteins are hydrolyzed by enzymes such as pepsin, trypsin and chymotrypsin. These catalysts act to speed up the hydrolytic reactions, thus making it possible for them to take place at the ordinary temperatures and under the normal acidity conditions of the organism. According to the peptide theory, these enzymes cause the hydrolysis of peptide bonds. If this theory is correct, then the same enzymes should hydrolyze simple peptides synthesized in the laboratory. For a long time protein chemists made intensive but vain efforts to create synthetic compounds that could be hydrolyzed by the enzymes, and their failure was interpreted by some as evidence against the peptide theory. In 1937, however, the author, working in Bergmann's laboratory at the Rockefeller Institute and using the carbobenzoxy method of peptide synthesis, succeeded in forming synthetic compounds which were specifically hydrolyzed at their peptide bonds by these enzymes. This finding strongly supported the Fischer-Hofmeister theory.

An additional support for the peptide theory is the finding that when the hydrolysis of protein is interrupted before the protein is entirely converted to amino acids, peptides can occasionally be isolated. The isolation of peptides obviously is not easy, for we have here the same difficulty of separating the components of a complex mixture that we encounter in the case of amino acids. The problem is, if anything, even more complicated, because the number of different peptides into which a protein may be split is considerably larger than the number of possible amino acids, and the amount of each peptide is very small. The new methods of chromatography appear well suited to the fractionation of peptides, and many investigators are now using them. Another valuable new approach to the problem has recently been provided by Lyman C. Craig of the Rockefeller Institute. He has developed a separation method based on the same general principles as are the familiar laboratory procedures for the extraction of a chemical substance from one solvent, such as water, by another solvent, such as ether. It is to be expected that this promising technique and the chromatographic method will form the main experimental lines of attack in the investigation of peptides obtained from proteins.

The brilliant work of the British chemist Frederick Sanger, which is the subject of the chapter by E. O. P. Thompson beginning on page 87, demonstrates the effectiveness of these methods. Sanger has succeeded in elucidating the complete structure of the important protein hormone insulin. A key step in this undertaking was his use of the reagent dinitrofluorobenzene. This substance combines readily with alpha-amino groups at the ends of insulin's peptide chains. The result of this combination is a compound called dinitrophenylinsulin (DNP-insulin). All the end alpha-amino groups in the compound are occupied by dinitrophenyl (DNP) groups. When the protein is subjected to hydrolysis by strong acid, all the peptide bonds are cleaved, but the linkages between the DNP group and the alpha-amino groups of the end amino acids are essentially unaffected. In other words, each end amino acid remains linked to a DNP group. Since the DNP group confers upon any compound in which it is present a distinctive yellow color, Sanger was able to separate the DNP-amino acids by chromatography and to determine the sequence in which they are linked together in the peptide chains of the insulin molecule.

The studies discussed thus far suggest that the protein molecule is a threadlike structure of several hundred amino acids, linked to one another through peptide bonds and strung out to form a chain (or several chains joined by disulfide bridges) of considerable length. There is good evidence that this description actually applies to insoluble proteins such as keratin or silk fibroin

66

and to a few soluble ones, notably the myosin of muscle and the fibrinogen of blood.

But most of the known proteins are not threadlike or fibrous. The enzymes, the protein hormones and all the blood proteins except fibrinogen are globular. They are soluble in water or salt solutions, but this characteristic solubility may readily be lost or decreased by subjecting the proteins to relatively small increases in temperature (up to 140 degrees Fahrenheit) or to mild acidity. This alteration in solubility is referred to as "denaturation." When the shape of such altered proteins is studied, it is found that they now approximate more closely the fibrous proteins. The denaturation of an enzyme or of a hormone usually deprives it of its characteristic biological activity. In some cases, if the exposure of the protein to the unfavorable conditions is not prolonged unduly, its denaturation can be reversed by restoring normal conditions. The protein then regains its characteristic solubility and its biological activity simultaneously.

It is obvious, therefore, that protein denaturation is associated with the conversion of a globular molecule to a rather fibrous one, and that this transformation is accompanied by the loss of some of the important biological properties of the protein. A natural deduction from these facts is that the peptide chains in the globular protein are coiled in a very specific way and that this characteristic folding is made possible by specific bonds between parts of the peptide chains. We can also make a deduction about the relative strength of these bonds. They must be much easier to rupture than ordinary peptide bonds, because the conditions required for denaturation are quite mild compared with those necessary for the cleavage of peptide bonds.

The nature of these special bonds has been the subject of much stimulating speculation. Among the several theories is one offered in 1936 by Alfred E. Mirsky of the Rockefeller Institute for Medical Research and Linus Pauling of the California Institute of Technology. They suggested that a major factor in conferring upon

67

the extended peptide chain of a protein its characteristic folding is the presence of "hydrogen bonds." This hypothesis has been successful in accounting for many of the known differences in the properties of "native" and denatured proteins. According to the theory, there are a multitude of bonds formed by the "sharing" of a hydrogen atom of an amino group with an oxygen atom of a carboxyl group. Taken individually these hydrogen bonds are weak, but in a protein molecule with several hundred amino-nitrogen atoms and a correspondingly large number of carboxyl-oxygen atoms, these weak bonds reinforce one another so that a stable structure results.

To the concept of the protein molecule as a long polypeptide chain or chains composed of many amino acids must therefore be added the idea that in each kind of protein the parts of the peptide chain have a characteristic internal arrangement which is responsible for that molecule's particular chemical and biological properties. Consequently the problem of protein structure involves not only the already formidable task of establishing the arrangement of the amino acids in the peptide chain, but even more difficult questions as to the nature and position of the bonds that are broken during denaturation.

Although the artificial creation of a protein molecule still lies beyond the powers of the chemist, it is no problem at all for the living organism. The living cell, whether of an amoeba or of a mammalian liver, performs the task of protein synthesis with rapidity and precision. Many organisms can use proteins foreign to their make-up, break them down to the component amino acids or peptides, and use the fragments to create their own characteristic proteins. Moreover, the proteins of a living organism are not laid down and kept intact throughout its life; rather there is a ceaseless breakdown and resynthesis of body proteins. In a sense, therefore, the problem of life is the problem of how living systems make proteins and how they constantly counteract the tendency toward protein degradation. Thus the study of the mechanisms by which cells synthesize proteins is perhaps the most challenging task of biochemistry.

A logical starting point for this investigation is the comparatively simple question of how living systems put two amino acids together to form a peptide bond. Many laboratories in this country are actively engaged in the exploration of this question. Although no clear-cut answer can yet be given, there are several hints as to its possible solution.

Among the views that have been entertained is the theory that in living cells the formation of peptide bonds is effected by the same enzymes that cause the breakdown of the peptide bonds after death. The principal support for this hypothesis has come from the demonstration that protein-splitting enzymes can indeed link two amino acids together to form a peptide bond. But this process will occur only under certain specific conditions. The most important of these is the necessity of counteracting the natural tendency of the protein-splitting enzymes to effect the hydrolysis of peptide bonds. A simple experimental procedure for achieving this reversal of hydrolysis is to choose a reaction which will result in formation of an insoluble peptide that comes out of solution as fast as it is formed. By taking advantage of this fact, it is possible to show without question that protein-splitting enzymes can catalyze the synthesis of peptide bonds.

The attractive feature of the theory is the fact that these enzymes exhibit a striking specificity of action on peptide linkages. In the case of the protein-splitting enzymes, the specificity of enzyme action depends largely on the nature of the amino acids that participate in the formation of the peptide bond. What is more, these enzymes act only at peptide linkages that involve amino acids of the L-type, which we noted earlier to be characteristic of the protein constituents. For example, one enzyme may catalyze peptide synthesis only when the amino acid that contributes the alpha-carboxyl group for formation of a peptide is L-tyrosine or L-phenylalanine. Replacement of either of these two amino acids

69

by any other amino acid, as far as tests made so far show, prevents action by the enzyme. Indeed, biochemists know of no other group of biocatalysts that compares with the protein-splitting enzymes in their selective action on peptide bonds. By virtue of this sharp specificity, therefore, these enzymes are well fitted to direct, precisely and reproducibly, the complex sequence of successive peptide syntheses required for the formation of a protein.

To observe their synthetic action, however, it is necessary to remove the product from the reaction. In other words, work must be put into the system to counteract the natural tendency of the enzyme to hydrolyze the product after it is synthesized. It follows that if enzymes do actually perform peptide synthesis in cells, this process must be coupled to another reaction that provides the necessary chemical energy. There is excellent reason for believing that the chemical energy comes from the breakdown of foodstuffs such as glucose by oxidation or fermentation, but it has not been possible as yet to demonstrate how the breakdown of glucose is linked directly with peptide-bond synthesis in cells.

Much attention has been paid in recent years to the suggestion of Fritz Lipmann of the Massachusetts General Hospital that peptide bond synthesis involves the intermediate formation of amino-acid derivatives of phosphoric acid. The source of these phosphoric-acid intermediates, according to Lipmann's theory, is a "high energy" phosphate carrier such as adenosine triphosphate (ATP). The latter substance has been shown to play a decisive role in the exchanges of chemical energy that occur during the metabolic breakdown of sugars. Work in several laboratories during recent years has provided experimental evidence that phosphate-containing intermediates may indeed be involved in the biological formation of certain amides, such as hippuric acid or glutamine. These amides are closely related structurally to the peptides; they differ from the latter only in that the CO-NH bond links an amino acid to a non-amino acid group. The intervention of ATP in the synthesis of the amide bond of glutamine, first demonstrated by the late John F. Speck of the University of Chicago, is of especial interest because this glutamic acid derivative is widely distributed in the tissues and fluids of animals and plants.

Although the experimental data offered in support of the Lipmann theory are impressive, they do not yet present a picture that would account satisfactorily for the specificity of peptide-bond formation. Each of the two theories discussed above thus contributes to a different, but equally essential, facet of the problem; it may well be that the two theories are complementary, rather than mutually exclusive. Such a view is supported by work begun in Bergmann's laboratory in 1937 and continued by the author at Yale University. These experiments have shown that protein-splitting enzymes will catalyze the hydrolysis and synthesis of peptide bonds. They have also shown that the same enzymes will cause reactions in which one of the two components contributing to a peptide bond may be replaced by another, without the need for the introduction of appreciable chemical energy but with the same specificity exhibited in synthesis and hydrolysis.

If these results should prove to have general significance, it would mean that an amide containing an amino-acid derivative linked to ammonia (e.g., glutamine) could exchange the ammonia for an amino acid or even a peptide. The energy for this process would come from the synthesis of glutamine, which, as Speck has shown, may involve a phosphate-containing intermediate. The specificity of the enzyme that catalyzes the exchange of the amide-nitrogen for the alpha-amino nitrogen of an amino acid or peptide would then determine the nature and sequence of the amino acids linked by peptide bonds in the final product. As a further consequence of this hypothesis, it would follow that a simple peptide composed of two or three amino acids would be transformed, in the presence of a suitable enzyme, into a longer chain by the replacement of one of the amino acids by a peptide. Energy would be required for the formation of the simple initial peptide, perhaps via a phosphate-containing intermediate, but the further course of peptide synthesis would be under the directive control of the highly specific enzymes that act as peptide bonds.

Another avenue of approach to the problem of how peptide bonds are formed is to seek out biological systems that exhibit unusual requirements for certain peptides, as compared with their demand for the individual amino acids of which these peptides are composed. If a bacterial cell, for example, uses a peptide for growth more efficiently than it does the amino acids, that would suggest that the rate of synthesis of the peptide controls the rate of utilization of the amino acids for protein formation. This approach is being explored in studies of the bacterial metabolism of peptides at Yale University by Sofia Simmonds in collaboration with the author. They may be expected to provide valuable biological material for the unequivocal testing of the various hypotheses relating to the mechanism of peptide-bond formation.

From all this it must be abundantly evident that the decisive discoveries in the study of the biological synthesis of proteins still lie in the future. Whatever the answer concerning the enzymatic mechanism of peptide-bond formation turns out to be, clearly it will provide only a part of the picture of the total process. What, for example, is the nature of the forces that confer upon the biologically interesting proteins, such as the enzymes and hormones, their characteristic physical, chemical and physiological properties? A denatured insulin molecule, though rendered inactive as a hormone, presumably still contains the same amino acids as the active molecule, and the peptide linkages that join these amino acids apparently have not been broken measurably. How, then, is the peptide chain molded in the living cell so as to form an active hormone with its specific attributes? Are we dealing here with an intricate mechanism whereby a model of the finished product is available as a matrix upon which the fragments are assembled?

These questions cannot be answered as yet, but it is well to remember that biochemistry is a relative newcomer among the scientific disciplines. Its growth has been meteoric, and it is exerting a decisive influence on the future development of all aspects of biology and their applications to medicine and agriculture. In the last analysis all the problems of biology meet in the unsolved problems concerning the structure and the mode of action of proteins. In groping for new experimental avenues into this great unknown, the protein chemist is thus probing into the basic questions of life. Whether he succeeds or not, he cannot help being filled with a sense of awe and humility in the face of what has justly been called the noblest piece of architecture produced by Nature—the protein molecule.

THE STRUCTURE OF PROTEINS

by Linus Pauling, Robert B. Corey
and Roger Hayward

THE HUMAN BODY is about 65 per cent water, 15 per cent proteins, 15 per cent fatty materials, 5 per cent inorganic materials and less than 1 per cent carbohydrates. A molecule of water consists of three atoms, two of hydrogen and one of oxygen. The structure of this molecule has been determined in recent years: each of the two hydrogen atoms is 0.96 Angstrom unit from the oxygen atom (an Angstrom unit is one ten-millionth of a millimeter), and the angle formed by the lines from the oxygen atom to the hydrogen atoms is about 106 degrees. Compared to this simple molecule, a protein molecule is gigantic. It consists of thousands of atoms, mostly of hydrogen, oxygen, carbon and nitrogen. The problem of how these atoms are arranged in a protein molecule is one of the most interesting and challenging now being attacked by workers in the physical and biological sciences.

The proteins are of especial interest not only because of their complexity of structure but also because of their variety and versatility. There are tens of thousands, perhaps as many as 100,000, different kinds of proteins in a single human body. They serve a multitude of purposes: collagen, a constituent of tendons, bones and skin, seems to have the main purpose of providing a framework which has suitable mechanical properties; hemoglobin, found inside of the red blood cells, has the primary function of combining with oxygen in the lungs and liberating it in the tissues; keratin, in the hair and in the epidermis, provides protection for the body, and in the fingernails it functions as a tool; pepsin, trypsin and many similar enzymes are involved in the digestion of

food; cytochrome c and other oxidation-reduction enzymes catalyze the oxidation of foodstuffs within the cells; the muscle protein
myosin plays an important part in the process of converting chemical energy into mechanical work. The tabulation could be continued almost indefinitely.

The story of the long campaign to unravel the structure of proteins is told in the chapter by Joseph Fruton. During the second
half of the nineteenth century it was found that proteins can be
broken down by boiling them in water for a long time or by treating them with acid or alkali, and that simple chemical substances,
called amino acids, can be obtained as the products of this treatment.

Just 50 years ago it was discovered by the German chemist Emil
Fischer that proteins consist of long chains of amino-acid residues.
(An amino-acid residue is the group of atoms that remains after a
molecule of water has been removed from a molecule of an amino
acid.) Long chains of amino-acid residues are called polypeptide
chains. The chains are usually very large; for example, in the molecule of ovalbumin, the principal protein of egg white, about 400
amino-acid residues form a single polypeptide chain. The number
of residues of amino acids of different kinds in a protein molecule
can be determined by chemical analysis of the protein; each molecule of ovalbumin has been found to contain about 19 glycine residues, about 35 alanine residues, about 9 tyrosine residues, and so
on for the 17 other kinds of amino acids that are represented.

In the study of the structure of a protein there are two questions
to be answered. What is the sequence of amino acids in the polypeptide chain? What is the way in which the polypeptide chain is
folded back and forth in the space occupied by the molecule? Significant progress has been made toward answering both of these
questions during recent years.

In this article we shall consider only the second question. The
experimental technique of greatest value in the attack on this
problem is that of X-ray diffraction. It was this technique that in

1914 enabled the Braggs (the late Sir William and his son Sir Lawrence, who is now director of the Davy Faraday Laboratory of the Royal Institution in London) to determine the structure of sodium chloride and other simple substances, and then of more complex inorganic substances, such as silicate minerals and metals, and of organic substances. Only half a dozen years after X-rays were first used for this purpose they were applied to proteins. At the Kaiser Wilhelm Institute in Berlin-Dahlem, R. O. Herzog and W. Jancke made X-ray diffraction photographs of hair, horn, muscle, silk and tendon. The results were disappointing—the definition of the photographs was so poor that it seemed a hopeless job to attempt to determine from them the positions of atoms.

Even though X-ray diffraction technique has since been immensely improved, such photographs still confront the investigator with a formidable task of deduction and computation. The X-ray diffraction picture of even so simple a substance as glycylglycine shows about 400 spots. Each of these spots represents a direction in which X-rays are strongly scattered by the atoms in the crystal. From several photographs of this sort a collection of about 800 characteristic intensity values can be obtained. The glycylglycine molecule contains 9 atoms other than hydrogen atoms; the hydrogen atoms do not scatter X-rays very strongly, and their positions are usually not well indicated by the X-ray method. The structure of the glycylglycine crystal can be described when three co-ordinates, the x, y and z co-ordinates, have been determined for each of the nine atoms. There are accordingly 27 atomic co-ordinates to be determined. The intensity of each X-ray reflection depends upon these co-ordinates, and it is possible from the 800 intensity values to determine all 27 of them with considerable accuracy. In this way each of the atoms, except the hydrogen atoms, in the glycylglycine crystal has been located to within about 0.02 Angstrom unit. This uncertainty is about 2 per cent of the distance between each atom and its nearest neighbors. We are, therefore, now in possession of a picture of the glycylglycine crystal in which we may repose reasonable confidence.

It is quite another matter to determine the structure of a more complex protein, such as keratin which makes up the fibers of hair. The polypeptide chains in fibrous proteins are about as complicated as those in ovalbumin. Chemical analysis of hair has shown that 18 different amino acids are represented in the keratin molecule, and that the repeating unit in the keratin fiber probably consists of about 300 amino-acid residues. Each amino-acid residue contains on the average about 9 atoms other than hydrogen; there are accordingly about 2,700 atoms to be located and 8,100 co-ordinates to be determined. Such a complex structure obviously cannot be determined from the ill-defined X-ray photograph of horsehair.

Despite this discouraging situation several investigators, most outstanding among them W. T. Astbury of the University of Leeds, continued to use X-rays in the study of the fibrous proteins that occur in plants and animals, and they collected a great deal of valuable information. Herzog and Jancke had observed that the X-ray patterns of hair, silk and tendon are quite different. The later investigators found that almost every one of the many fibrous proteins found in nature gives one or another of these three patterns. Such different proteins as hair, horn, fingernail, porcupine quill, muscle, epidermis, fibrinogen and bacterial flagella give similar X-ray photographs. This similarity strongly suggests that the configuration of the polypeptide chains in all of these proteins is the same; that, regardless of differences in the relative number and sequence of their amino-acid residues, the chains are folded or coiled according to a common pattern. Other fibrous proteins, such as silk and tendon, have different X-ray patterns, and their polypeptide chains must be coiled in different ways.

In 1937 it was decided in the Gates and Crellin Laboratories of Chemistry at the California Institute of Technology to attack the

77

problem of the structure of proteins along an indirect route—by learning enough about the nature of polypeptide chains to permit a good guess as to how the polypeptide chain would naturally fold itself to form a protein molecule or fiber. At that time the X-ray diffraction method had been successfully applied in the determination of the structure of hundreds of crystals, including some very complex ones such as the mineral beryl ($Be_3Al_2Si_6O_{18}$). No structure determination had, however, yet been made of any amino acid or any other simple substance closely related to the proteins.

The attack on these simple substances was begun, and by 1950 precise structure determinations had been made in these laboratories of three amino acids, three simple peptides (short chains of amino-acid residues), and several closely related substances. With the information provided by these structures it was possible to start work on the prediction of likely configurations for polypeptide chains. Since 1950 six more amino-acid and peptide structures have been determined at the California Institute of Technology, and several have been worked out in other laboratories also.

Much work was needed to learn the distances between the atoms, the angles between the chemical bonds, and other structural features. This had to be done with an accuracy corresponding to errors in atomic position not greater than about 0.02 Angstrom unit. The investigation of one crystal, the amino acid threonine, required the efforts of four post-doctoral research workers for an average of one full-time year apiece.

When several of these structures had been determined it was found that they were strikingly uniform from substance to substance. This uniformity permitted the reliable prediction of the dimensions of a polypeptide chain. The distances between atoms are believed to be reliable to about 0.02 Angstrom unit, and the angles between chemical bonds to within about three degrees.

One characteristic feature of the structure is of special importance. The six atoms of the so-called amide group (CCONHC)

78

are coplanar—they lie within a few hundredths of an Angstrom unit of a common plane. This planar amide group is a rigid part of the polypeptide chain; the amide group can be only slightly distorted from the planar configuration. The rigidity of the amide group greatly simplifies the problem of finding the ways in which the polypeptide chain can be folded.

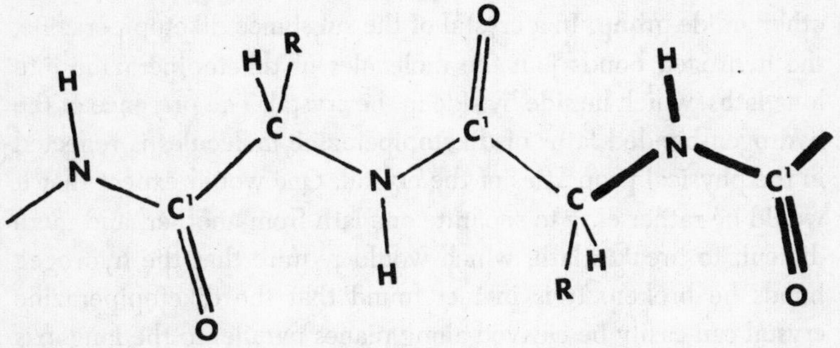

Polypeptide chain is shown here in conventional two-dimensional diagram. The amide group, the basic unit of the chain, is indicated by the heavy lines at right; this unit repeats in each "link" of the chain. The carbon marked C^1 is the carbon within the unit; the unmarked carbon is shared by adjoining units and establishes the linkage between them. The symbol R represents atoms or atomic groups in the side chains.

There are two alternative ways in which the atoms of the amide group can be arranged in a plane. One is called the trans configuration; in it there are carbon atoms at opposite corners of the group. The other is the cis configuration, in which the carbon atoms are at adjacent corners. There is evidence that the trans configuration is considerably more stable than the cis configuration, and the cis configuration is probably rare in the polypeptide chains of proteins.

A polypeptide chain of amide groups with the trans configuration might be folded in a great many ways. The bonds to the corner carbon atoms of the group are single chemical bonds, and the molecule may assume any one of various angles about the axis of each single bond. Of the resulting configurations, the satisfactory ones are those in which each amide group forms so-called hydrogen bonds with other amide groups. The hydrogen bond between two amide groups is a weak bond connecting a hydrogen atom and a nitrogen atom of one amide group with the oxygen atom of the other amide group. In a crystal of the substance diketopiperazine, the hydrogen bonds join the molecules of diketopiperazine into long laths, which lie side by side in the crystal. The presence of the hydrogen-bonded laths of diketopiperazine molecules is reflected in the physical properties of the crystal. One would expect that it would be rather easy to separate one lath from another, and more difficult to break a lath, which would require that the hydrogen bonds be broken. It is in fact found that the diketopiperazine crystal can easily be cleaved along planes parallel to the long axis of the laths.

By studying this crystal and others it has been shown that the average distance between a nitrogen atom and an oxygen atom connected by a hydrogen bond is 2.79 Angstrom units. It is accordingly reasonable to believe that an acceptable configuration for a polypeptide chain should be one permitting the formation of hydrogen bonds about 2.79 Angstrom units long.

The folding of the polypeptide chain that seems to occur most widely among proteins is shown in the illustration opposite. This configuration was discovered by analyzing the consequences of a simple assumption—that all of the amino-acid residues in the polypeptide chain are equivalent to one another, except for the difference in the nature of the side chains. Except for glycine the amino acids that occur in proteins are asymmetric; they are described as left-handed molecules. When asymmetric objects in space are joined together in such a way that every one has the same geometrical relationship to its neighbors, a helix is formed.

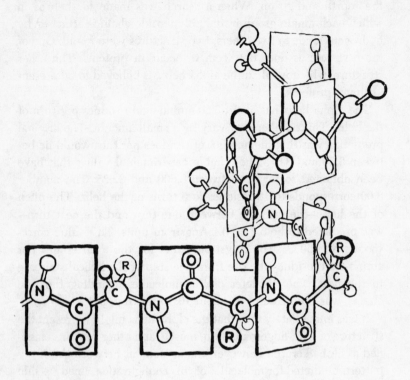

Alpha helix is the structural form of the polypeptide chain. It is dictated by the three-dimensional configuration of the linkage established by the carbon atom between each two amide groups. It can be seen that the amide groups, the atoms enclosed in the squares, are flat, while the side groups (R) project into the third dimension outside the planes of the amide groups. The angle in third dimension of the carbon linkage between the first two amide groups at lower left is ignored in this diagram.

An example is provided by a spiral (properly a helical) staircase; the first step is converted into the second step by moving it along the axis of the staircase and rotating it around the axis. The same operation converts the second step into the third, the third into the fourth and so on. When a search was made for helixes in which each amide group in the polypeptide chain is attached by hydrogen bonds to two others, two structures were found. One of these structures does not seem to occur in proteins. The other structure, which is called the alpha helix, is believed to be present in many proteins.

The alpha helix has about 3.60 amino-acid residues per turn of the helix. This number may vary by a small amount. The original prediction was that the number of residues per turn would lie between 3.60 and 3.67. The reliable experimental values that have been obtained so far lie between 3.600 and 3.625. The number 3.60 corresponds to 18 residues in 5 turns of the helix. The pitch of the helix—the distance between one turn and the next turn—was predicted to be 5.4 ± 0.1 Angstrom units. This value corresponds to 1.50 ± 0.03 Angstrom units for the axial length per amino-acid residue—the rise from one step of the helical staircase to the next. The diameter of the molecule, including the side chains, was predicted to be about 10.5 Angstrom units.

It was immediately seen that the alpha helix might represent the structure of hair, fingernail, horn, muscle and other proteins classified as alpha keratin. However, the agreement between the X-ray pattern predicted for molecules of this configuration, lined up side by side in parallel orientation, and the observed X-ray diagram was far from complete. Encouraging support then came from an unexpected quarter. The English investigators C. H. Bamford, W. E. Hanby and F. Happey had prepared X-ray photographs of some synthetic polypeptides in which all of the amino-acid residues in the polypeptide chain were chemically identical, and they published these photographs early in 1951. They were found to agree very well with the calculated X-ray pattern for a bundle of alpha helixes arranged in hexagonal packing. In particular, the positions and intensities of the X-ray reflections correspond very closely to the calculated values for a helix with 18 amino-acid residues in 5 turns.

There is a general similarity between the X-ray photograph of the synthetic polypeptide and the pattern of horsehair. This lends some support to the idea that alpha helixes are present in hair as well as in synthetic polypeptides, but the similarity is not close enough to be reliable. The convincing proof was provided by Max Perutz of the Cavendish Laboratory at Cambridge University. He pointed out that a strong X-ray reflection corresponding to a spacing of 1.5 Angstrom units should be observed for substances containing the alpha helix; the amino-acid residues, which are separated from one another by a distance of 1.5 Angstrom units along the axis of the helix, would co-operate with one another in scattering X-rays in the direction corresponding to this reflection. Perutz made X-ray photographs of synthetic polypeptides and many proteins, with the fibers oriented at the correct angle for this reflection to appear on the photographic plate, and he found that the reflection was in fact produced by the synthetic polypeptides and by hair, horn, fingernail, epidermis and other proteins which give X-ray photographs of the alpha-keratin type.

One striking difference between the X-ray photograph of horsehair and the expected pattern for an arrangement of alpha helixes in hexagonal packing is the presence of a strong reflection above and below the central image. In the corresponding photograph of the synthetic polypeptide there are strong reflections on either side of these points. About a year ago it was suggested independently by the workers at the California Institute of Technology and by F. H. C. Crick of Cambridge University that the strong vertical reflections result from the presence of molecules with the configuration of the alpha helix which are twisted about one another, to form what Crick calls coiled coils. This twisting of the alpha helix into a compound helix, shown in the illustration on page 85, might result from a small shortening and lengthening of hydrogen bonds, perhaps within the range 2.7 to 2.9 Angstrom units, in a regular way. A good correlation for all of the evidence is provided by the structure of alpha keratin, which is diagramed schematically on the same page. In this structure there are seven-strand cables, each about 30 Angstrom units in diameter, which are made up of six compound alpha helixes twisted about a central alpha helix. These seven-strand cables are arranged in hexagonal packing, and the interstices between them are occupied by additional alpha helixes.

It is of course evident that the X-ray photograph of horsehair does not provide enough information to settle the question of the structure of alpha keratin in complete detail. There seems to be little doubt, however, that hair and similar proteins are made up of polypeptide chains with the configuration of the alpha helix and that these chains are twisted about one another. It is not unlikely that the way in which the chains are twisted together is the one shown in the diagram, but there is a possibility that it may be somewhat different.

The simplicity of the helix as a structural element—the fact that it results automatically through the repetition of the most general symmetry operation which does not convert an asymmetric object into its mirror image—tempts us to look for helixes in larger structures. The search is rewarded when we look at electronmicrographs of bacterial flagella, the whiplike whiskers with which some species of bacteria are equipped. X-ray diffraction photographs have already told us that such flagella are of the alpha-keratin type, indicating the presence of alpha helixes. In the electronmicrograph, which provides magnification of better than 30,000 diameters, we can see that a flagellum consists of three strands, each 90 Angstrom units in diameter, twisted about one another. Although the way in which these strands are built out of alpha

How the polypeptide chain of amide groups (see diagrams on pages 79 and 81) forms a compound helix or coiled coil is shown in the diagram at left. At right is the design deduced for the structure of a bacterial flagellum, a structure visible under the microscope. It is a seven strand cable made up of seven strand cables in which the component strands are the coiled coils of polypeptide chains.

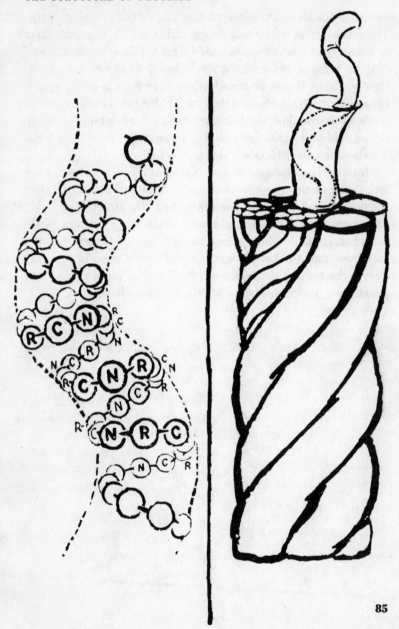

helixes is not known, one speculation immediately suggests itself. The seven-strand cables mentioned earlier are 30 Angstrom units in diameter; if a seven-strand cable were similarly made of seven of these seven-strand cables it would be 90 Angstrom units in diameter. Hence it may be found, when these flagella are subjected to more thorough study, that they can be described as three-strand ropes, each strand of which is a seven-strand cable built of seven-strand cables of alpha helixes. It is interesting that the bacterial flagella themselves form a still larger helix.

Through the development during the last quarter-century of the techniques of electron microscopy and X-ray diffraction, the time has now arrived when it is possible to track the structure of living organisms down through successively smaller orders of size, without a gap, from the whole animal through the cell to the atom. We may hope that the knowledge that will be obtained in this way during the coming decades will provide a far more precise and penetrating understanding of life than we now have.

THE INSULIN MOLECULE

by E. O. P. Thompson

Proteins, the keystone of life, are the most complex substances known to man, and their chemistry is one of the great challenges in modern science. For more than a century, as Joseph Fruton has related, chemists and biochemists have labored to learn their intricate structure. In the history of protein chemistry the year 1954 will go down as a landmark, for in that year a group of investigators finally succeeded in achieving the first complete description of the structure of a protein molecule. The protein is insulin, the pancreatic hormone which governs sugar metabolism in the body.

Having learned the architecture of the insulin molecule, biochemists can now go on to attempt to synthesize it and to investigate the secret of the chemical activity of this vital hormone, so important in the treatment of diabetes. Furthermore, the success with insulin has paved the way toward unraveling the structure of other proteins with the same techniques, and work on some of them has already begun.

The insulin achievement was due largely to the efforts of the English biochemist Frederick Sanger and a small group of workers at Cambridge University. Sanger had spent ten years of intensive study on this single molecule. When he commenced his investigation of protein structure in 1944, he chose insulin for several reasons. Firstly, it was one of the very few proteins available in reasonably pure form. Secondly, chemists had worked out a good estimate of its atomic composition (its relative numbers of carbon, hydrogen, nitrogen, oxygen and sulfur atoms). Thirdly, it appeared that the key to insulin's activity as a hormone lay in its

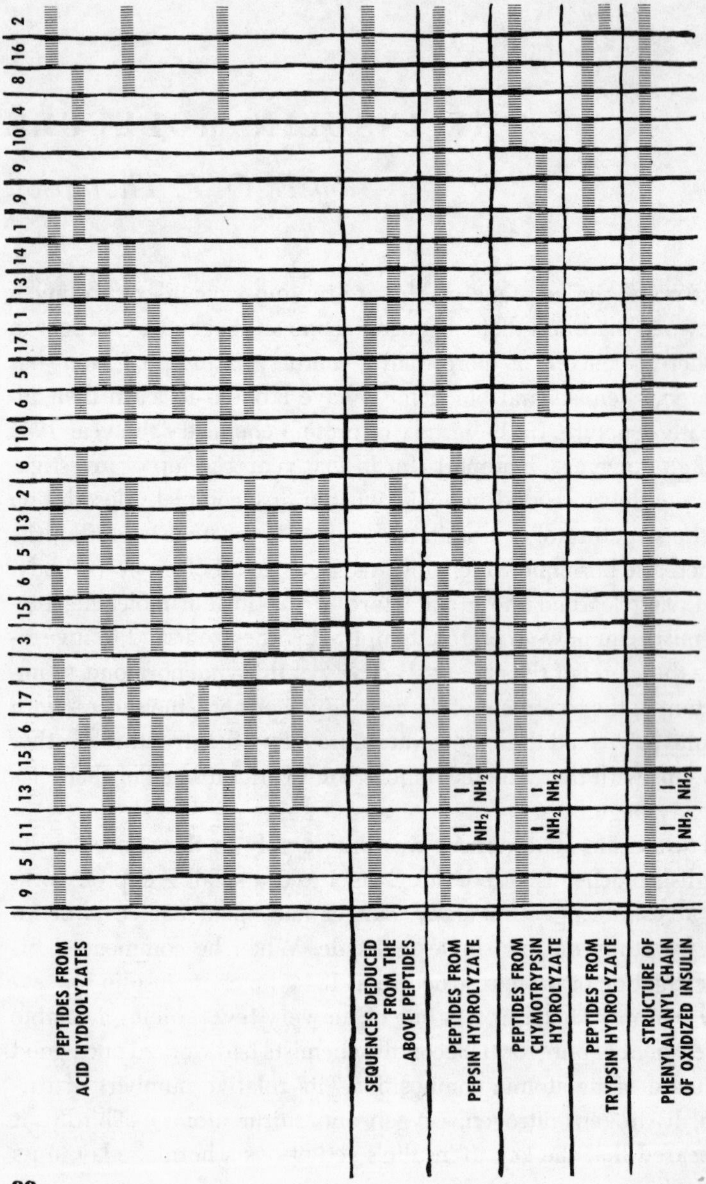
9 5 11 13 15 6 17 1 3 15 6 5 13 2 6 10 6 5 17 1 13 14 1 9 9 10 4 8 16 2
NH2
NH2
NH2
NH2
NH2
NH2
PEPTIDES FROM ACID HYDROLYZATES
SEQUENCES DEDUCED FROM THE ABOVE PEPTIDES
PEPTIDES FROM PEPSIN HYDROLYZATE
PEPTIDES FROM CHYMOTRYPSIN HYDROLYZATE
PEPTIDES FROM TRYPSIN HYDROLYZATE
STRUCTURE OF PHENYLALANYL CHAIN OF OXIDIZED INSULIN

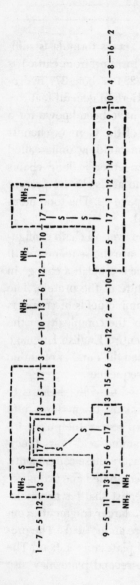

AMINO ACID GROUPS IN INSULIN

Key Number	Name	NUMBER OF GROUPS: in Phenylalanyl	in Glycyl
1	Glycine	3	1
2	Alanine	2	1
3	Serine	1	2
4	Threonine	0	2
5	Valine	3	2
6	Leucine	4	2
7	Isoleucine	0	1
8	Proline	1	0
9	Phenylalanine	3	0
10	Tyrosine	2	2
11	Asparagine	1	2
12	Glutamic Acid	2	2
13	Glutamine	2	0
14	Arginine	1	0
15	Histidine	2	0
16	Lysine	1	0
17	Cystine	2	4
		30	21

Complete molecule of insulin is depicted in the structural diagram immediately above. Each amino acid in the molecule is represented by a number and may be identified by reference to the table at right. The molecule consists of 51 amino acid units in two chains. One chain (top) has 21 amino acid units; it is called the glycyl chain because it begins with glycine (1). The other chain (bottom) has 30 amino acid units; it is called the phenylalanyl chain because it begins with phenylalanine (9). The chains are joined by sulfur atoms (S-S). How the sequence of amino acids in the phenylalanyl chain was deduced from fragments of the chain is shown in the chart on the page opposite. The numbered vertical columns indicate the position of each of the amino acids in the molecule. Each fragment is represented by a bar of vertical hatch lines across the columns corresponding to its component amino acids. The shorter fragments (group at the top) were obtained by hydrolyzing insulin with acid. The longer fragments (groups third, fourth and fifth from the top) were obtained with enzymes.

89

structure, for it contained no special components that might explain its specific behavior.

Insulin is one of the smallest proteins. Yet its formula is sufficiently formidable. The molecule of beef insulin (from cattle) is made up of 777 atoms, in the proportions 254 carbon, 377 hydrogen, 65 nitrogen, 75 oxygen and 6 sulfur. Certain general features of the organization of a protein molecule have been known for a long time, thanks to the pioneering work of the German chemist Emil Fischer and others. The atoms form building units called amino acids, which in turn are strung together in long chains to compose the molecule. Of the 24 amino acids, 17 are present in insulin. They are listed in the table on page 89. The total number of amino acid units in the molecule is 51.

Sanger's task was not only to discover the over-all chain configuration of the insulin molecule but also to learn the sequence of all the amino acids in the chains. The sequence is crucial: a change in the order of amino acids changes the nature of the protein. The number of possible arrangements of the amino acids of course is almost infinite. One can get some notion of the complexity of the protein puzzle by remembering that the entire English language is derived from just 26 letters (two more than the number of amino acids) combined in various numbers and sequences.

Sanger followed the time-honored method used by chemists to investigate large molecules: namely, breaking them down into fragments and then attempting to put the pieces of the puzzle together. A complete breakdown into the amino acid units themselves makes it possible to identify and measure these components. But this gives no clue to how the units are combined and arranged. To investigate the structure a protein chemist shatters the molecule less violently and then examines these larger fragments, consisting of combinations of two, three or more amino acids. The procedure is somewhat like dropping a pile of plates on the floor. The first plate may break into ten pieces; the second plate may also give ten pieces but with fractures at different places; the next plate may break into only eight fragments, and so on. Since the sample of protein contains billions of molecules, the experiment amounts to dropping billions of plates. The chemist then pores through this awesome debris for recognizable pieces and other pieces that overlap the breaks to show how the broken sections may be combined.

An amino acid consists of an amino group (NH_3^+), a carboxyl group (COO^-) and a side chain attached to a carbon atom. All amino acids have the amino and carboxyl groups and differ only in their side chains. In a protein molecule they are linked by combination of the carboxyl group of one unit with the amino group of the next. In the process of combination two hydrogen atoms and an oxygen atom drop out in the form of a water molecule and the link becomes CO—NH. This linkage is called the peptide bond. Because of loss of the water molecule, the units linked in the chain are called amino acid "residues." A group of linked amino acids is known as a peptide: two units form a dipeptide, three a tripeptide and so on.

When a peptide or protein is hydrolyzed—treated chemically so that the elements of water are introduced at the peptide bonds—it breaks down into amino acids. The treatment consists in heating the peptide with acids or alkalis. To break every peptide bond and reduce a protein to its amino acids it must be heated for 24 hours or more. Less prolonged or drastic treatment, known as partial hydrolysis, yields a mixture of amino acids, peptides and some unbroken protein molecules. This is the plate-breaking process by which the detailed structure of a protein is investigated.

One of the key inventions that enabled Sanger to solve the jigsaw puzzle was a method of labeling the end amino acid in a peptide. Consider a protein fragment, a peptide, which is composed of three amino acids. On hydrolysis it is found to consist of amino acids A, B and C. The question is: What was their sequence in the peptide? The first member of the three-part chain must have had a free (uncombined) amino (NH_3) group. Sanger succeeded in

91

finding a chemical marker which could be attached to this end of the chain and would stay attached to the amino group after the peptide was hydrolyzed. The labeling material is known as DNP (for dinitrophenyl group). It gives the amino acid to which it is attached a distinctive yellow color. The analysis of the tripeptide sequence proceeds as follows. The tripeptide is treated with the labeling material and is then broken down into its three amino acids. The amino acid which occupied the end position, say *B*, is now identified by its yellow color. The process is repeated with a second sample of the tripeptide, but this time it is only partly hydrolyzed, so that two amino acids remain as a dipeptide derivative colored yellow. If *B* is partnered with, say, *A* in this fragment, one knows that the sequence must be BA, and the order in the original tripeptide therefore was BAC.

Another tool that played an indispensable part in the solution of the insulin jigsaw puzzle was the partition chromatography method for separating amino acids and peptides, invented by the British chemists A. J. P. Martin and R. L. M. Synge. Obviously Sanger's method of analysis required separation and identification of extremely small amounts of material. With paper chromatography, which isolates peptides or amino acids in spots on a piece of filter paper, it is possible to analyze a mixture of as little as a millionth of a gram of material with considerable accuracy in a matter of days. As many as 40 different peptides can be separated on a single sheet.

With the knowledge that the insulin molecule was made up of 51 amino acid units, Sanger began his attack on its structure by investigating whether the units were strung in a single long chain or formed more than one chain. Among the components of insulin were three molecules of the amino acid cystine. The cystine molecule is unusual in that it has an amino and a carboxyl group at each end. Since such a molecule could cross-link chains, its presence in insulin suggested that the protein might consist of more than one chain. Sanger succeeded in proving that there were indeed two chains, which he was able to separate intact by splitting the sulfur links in the cystine molecule. Using the DNP labeling technique, he also showed that one chain began with the amino acid glycine and the other with phenylalanine.

Sanger proceeded to break each chain into fragments and study the pieces—especially overlaps which would permit him to build up a sequence. Concentrating on the beginning of the glycine chain, Sanger labeled the glycine with DNP and examined the peptide fragments produced by partial hydrolysis. In the debris of the broken glycine chains he found these sequences attached to the labeled glycine molecules: glycine-isoleucine; glycine-isoleucine-valine; glycine-isoleucine-valine-glutamic acid; glycine-isoleucine-valine-glutamic acid-glutamic acid. Thus it was evident that the first five amino acids in the glycine chain were glycine, isoleucine, valine and two glutamic acids. Similar experiments on the phenylalanine chain established the first four amino acids in that sequence: phenylalanine, valine, aspartic acid and glutamic acid.

Sanger and a colleague, Hans Tuppy, then undertook the immense task of analyzing the structure of the entire phenylalanine chain. It meant breaking down the chain by partial hydrolysis, separating and identifying the many fragments and then attempting to put the pieces of the puzzle together in proper order. The chain, made up of 30 amino acids, was by far the most complex polypeptide on which such an analysis had ever been attempted.

The bewildering mixture of products from partial breakdown of the chain—amino acids, dipeptides, tripeptides, tetrapeptides and so on—was much too complicated to be sorted out solely by chromatography. Sanger and Tuppy first employed other separation methods (electrophoresis and adsorption on charcoal and ion-exchange resins) which divided the peptide fragments into groups. Then they analyzed these simpler mixtures by paper chromatography. They succeeded in isolating from the fractured chain 22 dipeptides, 14 tripeptides and 12 longer fragments. These are shown in the chart on page 88. Although these were obtained only in microscopic amounts, they were identified by special techniques and the sequences of their amino acids were determined.

These were the jigsaw pieces that had to be reassembled. Just as in a jigsaw puzzle there are key pieces around which the picture grows, so in this case there were some key pieces as starting points. For instance, the chain was known to contain just one aspartic acid. Six peptides with this amino acid were found in the debris from partial breakdown of the chain [see chart]. The aspartic acid was attached to from one to four other amino acids in these pieces. Their sequences showed that in the original make-up of the chain the order must have been phenylalanine-valine-aspartic acid-glutamic acid-histidine.

Other sequences were pieced together in a similar way until five long sections of the chain were reconstructed. But this still left several gaps in the chain. Sanger and Tuppy now resorted to another method to find the missing links. They split the phenylalanine chain with enzymes instead of by acid hydrolysis. The enzyme splitting process yields longer fragments, and it leaves intact certain bonds that are sensitive to breakage by acid treatment. Thus the investigators obtained long chain fragments which bridged the gaps and revealed the missing links.

After about a year of intensive work Sanger and Tuppy were able to assemble the pieces and describe the structure of insulin's phenylalanine chain. Sanger then turned to the glycine chain and spent another year working out its structure, with the assistance of the author of this article. The glycine chain is shorter (21 amino acids) but it provided fewer clues: there were fewer key pieces that occurred only once, and two amino acids (glutamic acid and cystine) cropped up in so many of the fragments that it was difficult to place them unequivocally in the sequence.

One detail that remained to be decided before the structure could be completed was the actual composition of two amino acids in the chain. Certain amino acids may occur in two forms: e.g., glutamic acid and glutamine. Glutamic acid has two carboxyl (COO^-) groups, whereas glutamine has an amide ($CONH_2$) group in the place of one of the carboxyls. The difference gives them completely different properties in the protein. Similarly there are aspartic acid and asparagine. Now acid hydrolysis changes glutamine to glutamic acid and asparagine to aspartic acid. Consequently after acid hydrolysis of a protein one cannot tell which form these amino acids had in the original chain. The question was resolved by indirect investigations, one of which involved comparing the products obtained when the same peptide was broken down by acid hydrolysis and by enzymes which do not destroy the amide groups.

By the end of 1952 the two chains were completely assembled. There remained only the problem of determining how the two chains were linked together to form the insulin molecule. But this was easier said than done. As so often happens, what looked simple in theory had complications in practice.

The bridges between the chains, as we have noted, must be cystine, because this amino acid has symmetrical bonds at both ends. The fact that insulin contains three cystine units suggested that there might be three bridges, or cross-links, between the chains. It appeared that it should be a simple matter to locate the positions of the bridges by a partial breakdown of the insulin molecule which gave cystine-containing fragments with sections of the two chains still attached to the "bridge" ends.

When Sanger began this analysis, he was puzzled to find that the cystine-containing peptides in his broken-down mixtures showed no significant pattern whatever. Cystine was joined with other amino acids in many different combinations and arrangements, as if the chains were cross-linked in every conceivable way. Sanger soon discovered the explanation: during acid hydrolysis of the insulin molecule, cystine's sulfur bonds opened and all sorts of rearrangements took place within the peptides. Sanger and his as-

95

sociate A. P. Ryle then made a systematic study of these reactions and succeeded in finding chemical inhibitors to prevent them.

By complex analysis which employed both acid hydrolysis and enzyme breakdown, Sanger and his co-workers L. F. Smith and Ruth Kitai eventually fitted the bridges into their proper places and obtained a complete picture of the structure of insulin, shown in the highly schematic diagram on page 89. So for the first time the biochemist is able to look at the amino-acid arrangement in a protein molecule. The achievement seems astounding to those who were working in the field ten years ago.

To learn how insulin's structure determines its activity as a hormone is still a long, hard road. It will be difficult to synthesize the molecule, but once that has been accomplished, it will be possible to test the effect of changes in the structure on the substance's physiological behavior. Evidently slight variations do not affect it much, for Sanger has shown that the insulins from pigs, sheep and steers, all equally potent, differ slightly in structure.

The methods that proved so successful with insulin, plus some newer ones, are already being applied to study larger proteins. Among the improvements are promising new techniques for splitting off the amino acids from a peptide chain one at a time—clearly a more efficient procedure than random hydrolysis. The rate of progress undoubtedly will be speeded up as more biochemists turn their attention to the intriguing problem of relating the structure of proteins to their physiological functions.

PART 3 THE MOLECULE OF HEREDITY

I. THE CHEMISTRY OF HEREDITY
by Alfred E. Mirsky

A member of the Rockefeller Institute for Medical Research, Alfred Mirsky has been a recognized leader in biochemistry since 1930. He was born in Flushing, N. Y., educated at Harvard College and Harvard Medical School, and took his Ph.D. degree under the late Joseph Barcroft at Cambridge University. His early work was on hemoglobin. More recently, he has devoted his energy to the chemical nature of the chromosomes, the subject on which he writes here.

II. THE STRUCTURE OF THE HEREDITARY MATERIAL
by F. H. C. Crick

A British biologist, F. H. C. Crick originally set out to be a physicist. He decided to go into molecular biology after spending the war years designing mines for the British Admiralty. Awarded a fellowship by the Medical Research Council, he took further training at the Strangeways Laboratories in Cambridge, where he worked on the viscosity of the cytoplasm of chick fibroblasts. He is now a member of a Medical Research Council unit engaged in the study of biological molecules. Recently, he has been in the U. S., at the Polytechnic Institute of Brooklyn, working on X-ray diffraction of crystals of ribonucleic acid, the subject of this chapter.

III. THE REPRODUCTION OF VIRUSES
by Gunther S. Stent

The author is a chemist who switched to biology at the prompting of a physicist. Born in Berlin in 1924, Gunther S. Stent came to the U. S. in 1940, worked as a waiter, office boy and soda jerk and entered the University of Illinois. There he set out to be a chemist and did in fact, take his Ph.D. in that field. He was diverted to biology when he read "What is Life?" the distinguished little book by the great German physicist Erwin Schrödinger. Postgraduate fellowships at California Institute of Technology, Copenhagen and the Pasteur Institute in Paris gave him his background in his new field. He is now at the Virus Laboratory of the University of California, Berkeley.

IV. RICKETTSIAE
by Marianna Bovarnick

A biochemist who specializes in cell parasites, Marianna Bovarnick lectures at the College of Medicine of the University of the State of New York and conducts her research at the Veterans Administration Hospital in Brooklyn. She took her B.A. at Vassar College and a Ph.D. in biochemistry at Columbia University. During the war, she worked on a project dealing with the malarial cell parasites; later, at the Harvard School of Public Health, she began her work on the metabolism of rickettsiae which she reports here.

THE CHEMISTRY OF HEREDITY

by Alfred E. Mirsky

O UR ANCESTORS are present in our chromosomes, and they reach down to influence the chemistry of every cell in our bodies. That chemistry is the fundamental instrument of heredity there can be no doubt. The genes—the factors of heredity—must depend on the chemical composition of the chromosomes; the growth and division of the chromosomes are chemical processes, and it is by chemical processes that the chromosomes are able to influence the rest of the cell and so make manifest the hereditary factors. When, for example, a chromosome influences the color of a person's eyes, it must do so by taking part in some way in the chemical synthesis of a pigment.

The study of the chemistry of chromosomes is, therefore, a study of life at an elementary level. This article is an account of that fascinating investigation and what has been learned from it.

A living cell, animal or vegetable, has a nucleus within which is a certain number of chromosomes, the number depending on the species of animal or plant. The nucleus may occupy anywhere from less than one-hundredth to more than two-thirds of the volume of the cell; the rest of the material is the cytoplasm. The chromosomes have individuality: each one differs from all the others in the same set. Within the chromosomes are the genes, arranged in a linear order.

The formation of a new individual begins when the nuclei of an egg cell and a sperm cell fuse to form one cell. The fertilized egg now has two sets of chromosomes, one from each of the parent cells. The two sets are equivalent (except for those chromosomes concerned with sex), and thus there is a pair of each kind of chromosome. The cell then divides to start the building of the body cells of the new organism, and one can see through a microscope that the division proceeds in as orderly and complex a ritual as a courtly eighteenth-century ballet. Each chromosome grows in size and then splits lengthwise into two identical copies of the original. The couples are promptly separated by two sets of threads that pull them to opposite ends of the cell. The membrane surrounding the nucleus has meanwhile broken down, so that there is no barrier to impede their movement. The two sets of chromosomes become bunched at the opposite points. Once the sets are separated, the threads disappear and a membrane forms around each set. Now there are two nuclei, each containing a complete set of pairs of chromosomes, inherited from the two original parent cells. The two new nuclei are surrounded by cytoplasm, the nonnuclear material of cells. But since cytoplasm divides in a different way from the nucleus, the two daughter cells may have unlike quantities of it.

Thus, by division after division, the new body is built. Every cell of our bodies—each liver cell, brain cell, kidney cell—carries chromosomes and genes from both parents. In the fruit fly, *Drosophila,* we can see the phenomenon distinctly under the microscope. The chromosomes in the salivary gland cells of fruit-fly larvae are so large that we can make out their structural details and see that hereditary factors contributed by both parents are present in each pair of chromosomes.

Knowledge of the relation between chromosomes and heredity has come from two lines of investigation—breeding experiments and microscopic observations. It was the breeding experiments that showed that chromosomes carry hereditary factors. In recent years such experiments on the bread mold neurospora have shown most beautifully that hereditary factors in chromosomes have a precise controlling influence on many chemical processes in the cell.

100

The simplest and most direct evidence of the nucleus' far-reaching effect on the cell was provided by certain experiments made by the German biologist Joachim Hämmerling in 1931. He performed these experiments on Acetabularia, a little green plant consisting of a single large cell. It has the form of an umbrella, with the exceedingly small nucleus near the tip of the handle. If the hatlike top of the umbrella is cut off, a new one forms, looking just like the one removed. There are many varieties of Acetabularia, each having a distinctively shaped "hat." What Hämmerling found was that if he cut off the "hat" and the nucleus of one of these plants, and then planted in the remaining stump a nucleus taken from another variety of Acetabularia, the new "hat" that formed was like that of the second variety. It was the nucleus that decided what fashion "hat" was made. Hämmerling was even able to graft two different nuclei into the bottom of one "umbrella"; when he did so, the new "hat" was a compromise between the different shapes associated with the two nuclei.

The decisive influence of the nucleus has also been investigated by removing the nucleus from the amoeba, another single-celled organism. It has been known for many years that this operation slows down the metabolism of the cell. Recently Daniel Mazia of the University of California made such an investigation with tracer isotopes of phosphorus—an element well known to play a central role in cell metabolism. The speed with which the "tagged" atoms enter into new combinations in the cell measures the cell's rate of phosphorus metabolism. Mazia cut a number of amoebae in half, one half of the cell containing the nucleus and the other lacking a nucleus. He put the halves containing nuclei in one vessel and the enucleated cell halves in another. Then he supplied tagged phosphate to both lots for the same length of time. He found that the halves with nuclei took tagged phosphorus into their complex phosphorus-containing substances at a normal rate, but the nonnuclear halves took up much less phosphorus. This experiment again showed that the nucleus, though only a minute part of the amoeba, has a decisive influence on the phosphorus metabolism of the whole cell.

Naturally one is led to wonder whether the chemical apparatus by which the chromosomes control all these activities can be related to some special substance in them.

The chromosomes do indeed possess a special substance: desoxyribonucleic acid, called DNA for short. DNA is peculiar to the chromosomes; it is not found in any other part of the nucleus or in the cytoplasm. This was shown many years ago by the well-known "Feulgen reaction." The German biochemist Robert Feulgen had discovered that when DNA is warmed with strong acid and then treated in a certain way with acid fuchsin, it turns a brilliant crimson. He performed this experiment in a test tube and did not apply his test to living cells until some ten years later. When he did so, he found to his joy that the chemical treatment had not disintegrated the cells and that the network of chromosomes in each nucleus was boldly revealed in brilliant color. The rest of the cell was colorless. Ever since this experiment microscopists have been using the Feulgen reaction on all kinds of plant and animal cells. They have demonstrated that, in general, chromosomes are "Feulgen positive" and nothing else in a cell is. This means that DNA is present in chromosomes and not in other parts of the cell, or, strictly speaking, not in sufficient concentration to be Feulgen positive.

There is another remarkable fact about DNA. The various cells of the body differ greatly in chemical composition: the cells of the liver, kidney, heart, spleen and so on vary in the kind and amount of substances they contain. But every body cell, regardless of type, has the same amount of DNA in its nucleus. And the egg and sperm cells, containing only half as many chromosomes as body cells, have just one half as much DNA.

How does one measure the quantity of DNA in a nucleus? It was first done in domestic fowl in this way: One takes a specimen of blood from, say, a rooster and counts the number of red cells in a given volume. The amount of DNA in that volume is then measured and divided by the number of cells. This gives the quantity of DNA per red-cell nucleus: for the rooster it is 2.3 hundred-millionths of a milligram per nucleus. The sperm cells of a rooster, similarly analyzed, turn out to have half that amount—1.2 hundred-millionths of a milligram. To count the cells of solid tissues of the body, such as the liver, spleen, kidney or the like, the cells must first be dispersed in a fluid. To accomplish this, a piece of liver, for example, is immersed in citric acid and then disintegrated in a high-speed mixer. The cells are broken, but the nuclei remain intact. The nuclei, being heavier than the cell debris, can be separated by centrifugation. The clean nuclei are then dispersed in citric acid and counted. Once this has been done, the quantity of DNA per nucleus is calculated in the same way as in the case of red blood cells.

Such measurements have been made for the various tissues of a number of animals. In any one species of animal the quantity of DNA per nucleus is always about the same (within an error of 10 per cent), whether the cells come from the liver, pancreas, spleen or blood. But each species has its own characteristic DNA quota. In the frog, for instance, it is 15 hundred-millionths of a milligram per nucleus; in the shad, 2 hundred-millionths; in the green turtle, 5.3 hundred-millionths.

The experiments just described were done independently by two groups of investigators—in Strasbourg by the late André Boivin and his collaborators R. and C. Vendreley, and at the Rockefeller Institute for Medical Research by Hans Ris and myself. Ris and I have developed another method which measures the quantity of DNA in a single nucleus, rather than the average in a mass of nuclei. In this way some information can be had which is not obtainable by mass analysis.

The procedure depends upon the Feulgen reaction. Cells with nuclei colored by the Feulgen reaction are placed on a microscope slide, and a photoelectric cell is inserted in the eyepiece of the microscope to measure the amount of light absorbed by the pigment in the nucleus. By grading the amounts of light absorption registered for a series of nuclei of known DNA content, one gets a set of standards which relates the amount of DNA in a nucleus to the amount of light absorption. With this index it becomes possible to measure the DNA content of certain nuclei which could not otherwise be investigated.

There are, for example, some nuclei in the body which contain two or four sets of chromosome pairs instead of the usual one. They are called polyploid nuclei. These should, according to the rule, have respectively two and four times as much DNA as ordinary nuclei in the same animal. And the light-absorption analysis of individual cells shows that this is indeed the case. For instance, cells of the rat liver with one-set, two-set and four-set nuclei are found to have DNA contents in the same ratios—1:2:4.

There is, then, a certain quantity of DNA in each set of chromosomes, whether in the egg or sperm, twice this quantity in the sets of chromosome pairs present in most body cells and correspondingly more in the double and quadruple sets of chromosome pairs found in some cells. All this shows that DNA is closely associated with the hereditary factors of chromosomes and most likely forms part of the stuff of which the hereditary factors are made. The chromosomes of course contain other substances besides DNA (e.g., various proteins), but none of those other known constituents is distributed in nuclei in the same regular way.

It should be said that some investigators are convinced that certain cells of a developing embryo contain more than the normal amount of DNA for the organism. But at present it cannot be said whether their measurements are correct or are thrown off by some unconsidered technical point in the procedure. Even if such exceptions to the rule of DNA distribution do exist, they should not occasion surprise, considering how great are the possibilities for cell variation.

104

To the rule that DNA is restricted to the cell nucleus there is a clearly established exception, but it is an exception which may be said to prove the rule. DNA or something closely related to it has been found in the cytoplasm of egg cells of many organisms; indeed, these cells have far more of the substance in the cytoplasm than in the nucleus. Most egg cells are large with materials required for growth of the embryo. Long before fertilization these materials are fed into the egg from surrounding cells called "nurse cells." In 1936 M. Konopacki, a Polish biologist, showed that in certain animals the nurse cells produce DNA, which is passed into the egg cell along with other nutrient materials. It remains in the cytoplasm until an embryo forms. Recently D. C. Cooper at the University of Wisconsin found that the nurse cells in plants do the same thing, and he showed that the DNA was derived from the nuclei of the nurse cells. The DNA in the cytoplasm of an egg cell comes, then, from the nuclei of nurse cells and is destined ultimately for the nuclei of the embryo's cells. In other words, the DNA in egg cytoplasm is on its way from one nucleus to another. There is enough of this material in the cytoplasm of one egg cell, according to recent experiments of E. Zeuthen and E. Hoff-Jorgensen in Copenhagen, to supply the nuclei of the thousands of cells that will develop by division from the single fertilized egg.

Now let us consider some experiments which illuminate the dynamic role played by the DNA in the chromosomes. It all began with certain curious observations made by the English bacteriologist Fred Griffith. He was working with pneumococci, the bacteria that cause pneumonia. There are many varieties of pneumococci, and they are classified according to the chemical make-up of the gummy capsule that surrounds the cell, which is different for each type of pneumococcus. Each type reproduces its own kind of capsular gum. When grown under certain conditions, however, pneumococci lose their capsules and reproduce cells that lack capsules. What Griffith did was this: He used two cultures of pneumococci, one of encapsulated cells of type III, and another that had had capsules of type I but had lost the capsules. He killed the encapsulated type III cells by heating them in water. Then he injected these dead cells together with living nonencapsulated cells of type I into a mouse. After a suitable time Griffith examined the mouse and found that pneumococci of encapsulated type III were now growing at a great rate in its tissues! Surely the killed type III cells that had been injected into the mouse could not have multiplied. To make sure of this Griffith injected heat-killed encapsulated type I cells into many mice; in no instance did they multiply. The conclusion to be drawn was clear: It was the living, nonencapsulated type I cells that had multiplied, but they had been converted into encapsulated type III. The dead encapsulated cells had somehow transmitted their hereditary constitution to the living nonencapsulated cells. They must have passed along to the type I cells the ability to make type III capsular gum.

Griffith's results were confirmed by Martin Dawson at the Rockefeller Institute. He found a way of doing the experiment in a test tube: the mixed heat-killed and living cells were placed in a nutrient solution in a test tube and there, as well as in the mouse, the encapsulated, heat-killed cells transmitted their hereditary constitution to the living, nonencapsulated ones. Another important step was made by James L. Alloway, also at the Rockefeller Institute. Pneumococcus cells disintegrate when placed in bile salts; they seem to dissolve, and the fluid in the tube clears. Alloway found that the heat-killed encapsulated cells could transmit their hereditary constitution even after they had been dissolved. In short, it looked very much as if some substance in the cell, rather than the cell as a whole, was responsible for transmitting its hereditary constitution.

The problem now was to hunt for that substance in the disintegrated and dissolved debris of the cell. This problem was undertaken by O. T. Avery, Maclyn McCarty and Colin MacLeod at the Rockefeller Institute. They quickly eliminated the capsular gum itself as a possibility; when they destroyed the gum with an

106

enzyme which decomposes it, the cell debris was still able to transmit the hereditary property of forming a capsule. The investigators then removed from the debris the protein, which makes up the great bulk of material in the cell. They did so by a procedure which leaves the remaining compounds in the solution undamaged. That operation eliminated the protein as a suspect, for what was left of the heat-killed and decimated cell could still transmit its heredity.

With the capsular gum and cell protein out of the way, it became apparent that the effective substance might well be DNA. And further experiments indicated that indeed it was. When the DNA in the remaining material of the cell was decomposed by a purified enzyme known to act specifically on DNA, the debris finally lost its ability to promote the manufacture of capsular gum.

The action of DNA is highly specific. If the DNA derived from another type of pneumococcus is added to nonencapsulated cells, the cells that finally multiply are of the type from which the DNA was derived. There must be a special kind of DNA in each type of pneumococcus.

Transmission of hereditary characteristics in pneumococci by means of DNA provides a beautiful example of one of the fundamental principles of heredity. What is transmitted in us from one generation to the next is not a characteristic eye pigment or blood type or other hereditary trait. Rather, it is a set of factors in chromosomes which are able to influence the activities of the cells so that certain eye pigments and certain substances responsible for blood types are produced. In the pneumococcus the DNA of the pneumococcal chromosomes influences the cell in which it is placed to make a particular kind of capsular gum.

What is the chemical nature of this potent substance? DNA was first discovered in the nucleus by the Swiss biochemist Friedrich Miescher in 1869. He was working with pus cells in the laboratory of Felix Hoppe-Seyler, one of the leading biochemists of the time. At first he had done some experiments on these cells along a line

107

suggested by his teacher. When they did not turn out well, he investigated on the same cells the effect of pepsin, the enzyme of gastric juice which digests proteins. Unlike most biochemists, then or now, Miescher made a practice of examining carefully under a microscope the cells from which he extracted substances. As the pepsin in dilute acid decomposed the proteins of the pus cells, Miescher saw under the microscope that while the structure of the cell as a whole disintegrated, the nucleus remained essentially intact, though it shrank in size. When the peptic digestion was complete, most of the materials of the pus cells had gone into solution. Miescher made a chemical analysis of the residue, consisting of shrunken cell nuclei, and found its composition different from anything else that had previously been prepared from cells. He called the material "nuclein," because it was located in the cell nucleus.

Hoppe-Seyler, at first skeptical about the discovery, soon convinced himself that the work was sound. He himself prepared from yeast cells a substance similar to nuclein. In the meantime Miescher had returned to his native Swiss city, Basel, and there continued his study of nuclein. Basel was fortunately a most suitable place for chemical investigation of the cell nucleus. At that time the Atlantic salmon still swam up the Rhine as far as the falls just above Basel. The fish came up the river to spawn, and when they reached Basel their testes were large with sperm. Nearly every spring Miescher would conduct a sperm-collecting campaign, for salmon sperm are in many respects the most suitable cells for chemical investigation of the nucleus. They are exceedingly rich in DNA; it makes up 50 per cent of their dry weight.

With this favorable material Miescher soon began to make great progress. He found that he could remove the cytoplasm from the sperm cells by immersing them in dilute acid, thereby obtaining clean, well-formed nuclei. It was no difficult matter to extract from the nuclei pure, protein-free DNA. Miescher determined its content of nitrogen, phosphorus, carbon, oxygen and hydrogen. By this time it was clear that "nuclein" was an acid, and another investigator suggested that the protein-free substance be called "nucleic acid."

Miescher was a thorough investigator, not easily satisfied with his own achievements, and when he died in middle age much of his experimental work was found unpublished in his notebooks. In 1897 friends gathered these notes, along with his published papers, into a volume which investigators in this field find well worth poring over today.

Of the other biochemists who entered the field of investigation of the cell nucleus during Miescher's time, two of the most notable were Albrecht Kossel in Heidelberg and P. A. Levene at the Rockefeller Institute. In contrast to Miescher, who worked by himself, both Kossel and Levene had large laboratories and many collaborators—and for the type of problem which now came under investigation, many collaborators were needed.

These investigators, all skillful organic chemists, set themselves the task of unraveling the structure of the nucleic acid molecule. It is a large molecule, consisting of half a dozen different, moderate-sized molecules joined together. The first problem was to take apart the large nucleic acid molecule and identify its component molecules. This had to be done gently, for the smaller molecules are themselves quite complex, and rough handling might decompose them. The safest way is to use enzymes, the tools that the organism employs. For some purposes it is possible to use a relatively rough procedure, such as treatment with hot, strong acid.

When the submolecules had been separated, they were examined to see whether they accounted for all the elements found in the large molecule. All the nitrogen could be accounted for by a group of nitrogenous submolecules, of a kind related to uric acid and caffeine. Four of these nitrogenous molecules were found, distinctly different from one another but belonging to the same family of substances. The phosphorus of DNA could be accounted for by the presence of phosphoric acid, which also explains why

109

DNA is an acid. Another submolecule found in DNA is a 5-carbon sugar. From these three types of submolecules DNA is constructed in this way: The 5-carbon sugar molecules are linked together in chains by phosphoric acid links, and to each sugar molecule in the chain is attached one or another of the four nitrogen-containing submolecules. (A fifth nitrogen-containing molecule has recently been found; the amount varies strikingly in different kinds of DNA.)

An intact molecule of DNA is a very large, complicated structure: it may contain as many as 3,000 molecules of the 5-carbon sugar. DNA is an example of what is nowadays called a high polymer. Familiar examples of high polymers are nylon and other substances of which fibers are formed. The characteristic of a high polymer is that some chemical unit is linked together repeatedly to form a big structure. In nylon the unit is relatively simple, there being but one type of submolecule. In DNA the units are far more complex. To learn how they are polymerized to form a giant molecule is a formidable task which has not yet been accomplished. When it is, we shall understand better how DNA functions in the chromosome.

The success of the Feulgen reaction in making chromosomes visible depends upon the fact that DNA is a polymer. When subjected to the procedure of the Feulgen reaction, the polymerized DNA remains insoluble and so becomes stained where it is located in the cell. When DNA that has been depolymerized (i.e., partly decomposed) is treated by the same procedure, it goes into solution; if it were not a polymer it would be washed out of the cell by the Feulgen process.

The effectiveness of DNA as a transmitter of heredity also depends upon its being polymerized. This can be seen in experiments with pneumococci. When the DNA of the heat-killed encapsulated pneumococcus is depolymerized, its ability to transmit the hereditary constitution of the cell is lost.

Besides DNA, every cell possesses another type of nucleic acid.

110

It is known as ribonucleic acid (RNA). Like DNA, it is composed of phosphoric acid, nitrogen submolecules and a 5-carbon sugar. But RNA's sugar molecule (called ribose) is very different from DNA's (called desoxyribose). It has one more oxygen atom, and this has a big effect on the molecule's properties. Since as much as 48 per cent of a nucleic acid is sugar, and the sugar occupies a central position in the molecule's structure, the difference between the sugars probably is responsible for the many differences between the behavior of RNA and that of DNA.

RNA has a different location in the cell and seems to be concerned with quite different biological functions. It is located largely in the cytoplasm, and it seems to be concerned with synthesis of protein. Protein synthesis is of course one of the central problems in biology, because proteins constitute a large part of living matter, because in the form of enzymes they control nearly all the dynamic processes of the cell, and because they are so complex that they have so far defied all efforts of chemists to solve the riddle of how they are made. Hence RNA is of intense interest to chemists and biologists.

RNA was found in yeast soon after Miescher's discovery of DNA. Since DNA was usually prepared from the cells of animals (fish sperm and the calf thymus gland), while RNA was usually prepared from plant cells (yeast), for many years DNA was known as animal nucleic acid and RNA was known as plant nucleic acid. The first step toward correcting this error came when Feulgen applied his color reaction and found that the nuclei both of plant cells and of animal cells contained DNA. He also stained cells in other ways to try to detect RNA, and he concluded that RNA also probably was present in both plant and animal cells, in this case in the cytoplasm.

To settle more definitely the question of where DNA and RNA are located in cells, Feulgen's pupil Martin Behrens made preparations of isolated nuclei and isolated cytoplasm. For this experiment he used, among other cells, those of the embryo of the rye plant. In order to avoid losing or transferring any of the substances from the nucleus or the cytoplasm while he was separating them, he decided to carry out the separation in the absence of water. He began by freezing the tissue and drying it in a vacuum while frozen. Then he ground the material in a nonaqueous fluid to break up the cells and release the nuclei from the cytoplasm in which they were embedded. Cell walls break more readily than nuclear walls, so it is possible to break up most of the cells without much breakage of nuclei. Next Behrens suspended the disintegrated material in a series of fluids of different density, first floating away the lighter debris and then floating the nuclei away from the heavier debris. This is a laborious process, but Behrens was patient and skillful. Finally he evaporated the fluids and found at last that he had obtained clean nuclei free of cytoplasm and cytoplasm free of nuclei. Those who have repeated his procedure know that it must have given him great satisfaction to put the powders consisting of separated nuclei and of cytoplasm into vials and label them. To have such preparations, in powdered form and in neatly labeled vials, is the dream of every chemist.

From these separated parts of the cell Feulgen and Behrens proceeded to extract nucleic acids and to identify them chemically. They found DNA in the nuclei and RNA in the cytoplasm. It was clear that DNA is in general confined to the nucleus and that at least the bulk of RNA is in the cytoplasm of both animal and plant cells.

For a more precise localization of nucleic acids in the cell further microscopic observations were required, and these were soon made by Jean Brachet in Brussels and Torbjörn Caspersson in Stockholm. They located the nucleic acids, as Feulgen had, by means of chemical properties which can be detected in a minute amount of material under the microscope. Brachet's method depended upon the presence of phosphoric acid in nucleic acids, Caspersson's on the presence of nitrogen containing submolecules. After investigating many different kinds of cells, they found that there is some RNA in the nucleus, especially in a body called the nucleolus which is attached to a certain chromosome, and that the chromosomes themselves contain some RNA. The amount of RNA in the nucleolus and cytoplasm varies considerably from cell to cell, and in a highly significant way. Certain physiologically active cells, such as those of the heart, skeletal muscles and kidney, contain very little. But cells active in the synthesis of protein, such as those of the glands and those growing rapidly, have a high concentration of RNA in the nucleolus and cytoplasm. Of the large cells lining the stomach those that synthesize pepsin (a protein) have a large amount of RNA, whereas those that form hydrochloric acid have little.

All this certainly indicates very strongly that in some way, not yet understood, RNA plays a part in the synthesis of protein. And this seems especially true of the RNA of the nucleus. Holger Hydén in Sweden has seen under the microscope evidence that in the living cell RNA moves out of the nucleus into the cytoplasm. This may well be one of the mechanisms by which the nucleus influences the surrounding cytoplasm. The clearest sign that the RNA of the nucleus is particularly active comes from an experiment done by R. Jeener in Brussels. He exposed cells to phosphate containing tagged phosphorus and determined that much more phosphorus was incorporated in the RNA of the nucleus than in that of the cytoplasm.

The extreme variation in the amount of RNA contained in an organism's various cells is in striking contrast to the constancy of DNA in the nuclei. The cells of the pancreas of a fowl, for example, have several times as much RNA as do those of the kidney, whereas the nuclei of the two kinds of cells have the same amount of DNA.

Nucleic acids in a cell are not unattached. They are combined with proteins. Very little is known about the protein combinations of RNA. The proteins attached to DNA, on the other hand, were investigated by Miescher and by those who followed him. In the salmon sperm nucleus Miescher discovered, combined with the phosphoric acid of DNA, an unusual protein—far more basic and much simpler in construction than other proteins. It lacked many of the amino acids that are present in most protein molecules. The name of this protein is familiar to diabetics: it is protamine, which is now added to insulin to keep that substance in the blood for a longer period. This is an excellent example of how unpredictable the applications of science frequently are. Who could have anticipated that the strange protein which Miescher discovered in salmon sperm would be combined with a hormone of the pancreas for the treatment of diabetes?

Kossel made an extensive study of the protamines in fish sperm. His work on these simple proteins had a considerable influence on our understanding of proteins in general. Kossel found other basic proteins in the nuclei of red blood cells and of calf thymus, and the author later found them in nuclei of liver, kidney, pancreas and other cells. They are probably present in all cell nuclei. Most of these proteins are somewhat less basic, more complex and larger than those in sperm. During the formation of sperm cells in the testes, the more complex basic proteins in the cells from which they are made are replaced by the simpler protamines. The functions of a sperm cell are to reach the egg and transmit hereditary factors; all the equipment not essential to those functions is trimmed down to a minimum. In fact, the sperm nucleus consists of little more than DNA and its attached basic protein. Even the basic protein is trimmed down to essentials; in the fully formed sperm all that remains of it is the basic part that combines with the phosphoric acid of DNA.

The linear arrangement of the hereditary factors in a chromosome implies that DNA, which is an essential part of these factors, is held in a chromosome in a definite and precise manner. We have found that it is attached to a protein which forms part of the structure of the chromosome. From a mass of isolated chromosomes in a test tube it is possible to extract all the strongly basic protein. This is done with concentrated saline, made slightly acid. Even with the basic protein missing, the chromosomes appear unchanged when examined under the microscope, and they retain their DNA when immersed in a neutral medium. This shows clearly that the DNA is still attached to something in the chromosomes, for in this medium it is freely soluble. If it were not so bound, the DNA would simply float away from the chromosomes. That the material to which the DNA is bound is a protein was proved by treating the chromosomes with pure crystalline trypsin, which digests protein. The polymerized DNA was set free and formed a thick gel. When, on the other hand, we broke down the DNA in chromosomes with an enzyme which digests the nucleic acid, there was left a protein which could be seen as a mass of minute coiled threads, quite unlike chromosomes in appearance. It had been deformed and condensed by its separation from DNA. It is the combination of this protein with DNA (to which basic protein also is attached) that forms the chromosome as seen under the microscope. If either DNA or the structural protein is digested, the structure of the chromosome disintegrates.

The amount of structural protein in the chromosomes, unlike that of DNA, is not constant but depends on the over-all activity of the cell. Cells with abundant, metabolically active cytoplasm (e.g., those of the liver or kidney) have a relatively large amount of structural protein in their chromosomes. On the other hand, a cell such as the lymphocyte, with only a scanty layer of cytoplasm around its nucleus, has only one-fifth as much. The metabolically sluggish red blood cell contains less than one-tenth as much.

The fact that the quantity of structural protein in the chromosomes is related to the over-all metabolism of the cell suggests that the structural protein may itself be metabolically active. Experiments show that this is indeed the case. The metabolic activity of the protein was measured by supplying tagged nitrogen, built into an amino acid (glycine). The amino acid can be injected into rats or mice and the fate of the tagged atoms followed in their cells. Einar Hammarsten in Stockholm found that the tagged nitrogen

115

was taken up by the nuclear proteins much more rapidly than by DNA. In our laboratory, carrying the experiment a step further, we showed that structural protein took up nitrogen much more rapidly than did basic protein.

Since the amount of the metabolically active structural protein varies considerably in different nuclei of an organism, it follows that the chromosomes of the different cells must vary in their activity. This also has been confirmed with tagged nitrogen of glycine. Liver and kidney cells of a mouse, for example, have equal quantities of DNA, but the DNA in liver chromosomes takes up nitrogen three times as fast as that in the kidney. Even in the same cell chromosome activity varies during different physiological states. The cells of a digestive gland, such as the pancreas, become far more active when an animal is fed, and when the cells are more active, the DNA of their chromosomes takes up 50 per cent more tagged nitrogen. The degree of activity of a chromosome must depend on its surroundings.

The immediate environment of the chromosomes is the cell nucleus. To understand how the chromosomes function we must know the conditions within the nucleus. The effects of chromosome activity are seen in the cytoplasm. The cytoplasm of each type of cell is especially equipped to carry out its specific functions: muscle-cell cytoplasm contains the contractile protein myosin; red-blood-cell cytoplasm has the oxygen-carrying pigment hemoglobin; pancreas-cell cytoplasm has the digestive enzyme trypsin, and so on. In each type of cell the chromosomes are acting on a differentiated cytoplasm. If such a system is to work effectively and harmoniously, the parts must be integrated; there is need for a feedback from the cytoplasm to chromosomes so that the latter's activity is adjusted to the cytoplasm's special requirements. The place to look for evidence of such a feedback is in the nuclear composition.

Does the differentiation of the cytoplasm change the nucleus? There is every indication that it does indeed. The enzymes in nuclei

116

of different cell types of an organism vary, as do those in the cytoplasm. Even when the cytoplasm of a given type of cell has a special enzyme, the same enzyme can occasionally be found in the cell's nucleus as well. For example, the enzyme arginase, which enables liver cells to form urea, is present in both the cytoplasm and the nuclei of those cells. Since changes in the cell environment may produce marked changes in the cytoplasm, it follows that they may also alter the composition of the nucleus, and this has in fact been found to be the case.

Thus the relationship between the nucleus and the cytoplasm is a two-way affair. The hereditary factors in the chromosomes govern the cell as a whole, but the cell in turn influences conditions within the nucleus and so modifies the activity of its chromosomes. Our knowledge of this reciprocal influence, and of the chemistry of the interaction between nucleus and cytoplasm, is still vague, but obviously this is a central problem for our understanding of the cell.

THE STRUCTURE OF THE
HEREDITARY MATERIAL

by F. H. C. Crick

Viewed under a microscope, the process of mitosis, by which one cell divides and becomes two, is one of the most fascinating spectacles in the whole of biology. No one who watches the event unfold in speeded-up motion pictures can fail to be excited and awed. As a demonstration of the powers of dynamic organization possessed by living matter, the act of division is impressive enough, but even more stirring is the appearance of two identical sets of chromosomes where only one existed before. Here lies biology's greatest challenge: How are these fundamental bodies duplicated? Unhappily the copying process is beyond the resolving power of microscopes, but much is being learned about it in other ways.

One approach is the study of the nature and behavior of whole living cells; another is the investigation of substances extracted from them. This chapter will discuss only the second approach, but both are indispensable if we are ever to solve the problem; indeed some of the most exciting results are being obtained by what might loosely be described as a combination of the two methods.

Chromosomes consist mainly of three kinds of chemical: protein, desoxyribonucleic acid (DNA) and ribonucleic acid (RNA). (Since RNA is only a minor component, we shall not consider it in detail here.) The nucleic acids and the proteins have several features in common. They are all giant molecules, and each type has the general structure of a main backbone with side groups attached. The proteins have about twenty different kinds of side groups; the nucleic acids usually only four (and of a different type). The smallness of these numbers itself is striking, for there is no obvious chemical reason why many more types of side groups should not occur. Another interesting feature is that no protein or nucleic acid occurs in more than one optical form; there is never an optical isomer, or mirror-image molecule. This shows that the shape of the molecules must be important.

These generalizations (with minor exceptions) hold over the entire range of living organisms, from viruses and bacteria to plants and animals. The impression is inescapable that we are dealing with a very basic aspect of living matter, and one having far more simplicity than we would have dared to hope. It encourages us to look for simple explanations for the formation of these giant molecules.

The most important role of proteins is that of the enzymes—the machine tools of the living cell. An enzyme is specific, often highly specific, for the reaction which it catalyzes. Moreover, chemical and X-ray studies suggest that the structure of each enzyme is itself rigidly determined. The side groups of a given enzyme are probably arranged in a fixed order along the polypeptide backbone. If we could discover how a cell produces the appropriate enzymes, in particular how it assembles the side groups of each enzyme in the correct order, we should have gone a long way toward explaining the simpler forms of life in terms of physics and chemistry.

We believe that this order is controlled by the chromosomes. In recent years suspicion has been growing that the key to the specificity of the chromosomes lies not in their protein but in their DNA. DNA is found in all chromosomes—and only in the chromosomes (with minor exceptions). The amount of DNA per chromosome set is in many cases a fixed quantity for a given species. The sperm, having half the chromosomes of the normal cell, has about half the amount of DNA, and tetraploid cells in the liver, having twice the normal chromosome complement, seem to have twice the amount of DNA. This constancy of the amount of DNA is what one might expect if it is truly the material that determines the hereditary pattern.

Then there is suggestive evidence in two cases that DNA alone, free of protein, may be able to carry genetic information. The first of these is the discovery that the "transforming principles" of bacteria, which can produce an inherited change when added to the cell, appear to consist only of DNA. The second is the fact that during the infection of a bacterium by a bacteriophage the DNA of the phage penetrates into the bacterial cell while most of the protein, perhaps all of it, is left outside.

DNA can be extracted from cells by mild chemical methods,

Fragment of chain of desoxyribonucleic acid shows the three basic units that make up the molecule. Repeated over and over in a long chain, they make it 1,000 times as long as it is thick. The backbone is made up of pentose sugar molecules (marked by the dashed-line square at bottom left), linked by phosphate groups (square at bottom right). The bases (square at top), adenine, cytosine, guanine and thymine (not shown), protrude off each sugar in irregular order.

and much experimental work has been carried out to discover its chemical nature. This work has been conspicuously successful. It is now known that DNA consists of a very long chain made up of alternate sugar and phosphate groups (see diagram on page opposite). The sugar is always the same sugar, known as desoxyribose. And it is always joined onto the phosphate in the same way, so that the long chain is perfectly regular, repeating the same phosphate-sugar sequence over and over again.

But while the phosphate-sugar chain is perfectly regular, the molecule as a whole is not, because each sugar has a "base" attached to it and the base is not always the same. Four different types of base are commonly found: two of them are purines, called adenine and guanine, and two are pyrimidines, known as thymine and cytosine. So far as is known the order in which they follow one another along the chain is irregular, and probably varies from one piece of DNA to another. In fact, we suspect that the order of the bases is what confers specificity on a given DNA. Because the sequence of the bases is not known, one can only say that the *general* formula for DNA is established. Nevertheless this formula should be reckoned one of the major achievements of biochemistry, and it is the foundation for all the ideas described in the rest of this chapter.

At one time it was thought that the four bases occurred in equal amounts, but in recent years this idea has been shown to be incorrect. E. Chargaff and his colleagues at Columbia University, A. E. Mirsky and his group at the Rockefeller Institute for Medical Research and G. R. Wyatt of Canada have accurately measured the amounts of the bases in many instances and have shown that the relative amounts appear to be fixed for any given species, irrespective of the individual or the organ from which the DNA was taken. The proportions usually differ for DNA from different species, but species related to one another may not differ very much.

Although we know from the chemical formula of DNA that it is a chain, this does not in itself tell us the shape of the molecule, for the chain, having many single bonds around which it may rotate, might coil up in all sorts of shapes. However, we know from physical-chemical measurements and electronmicroscope pictures that the molecule usually is long, thin and fairly straight, rather like a stiff bit of cord. It is only about 20 Angstroms thick (one Angstrom = one 100-millionth of a centimeter). This is very small indeed, in fact not much more than a dozen atoms thick. The length of the DNA seems to depend somewhat on the method of preparation. A good sample may reach a length of 30,000 Angstroms, so that the structure is more than 1,000 times as long as it is thick. The length inside the cell may be much greater than this, because there is always the chance that the extraction process may break it up somewhat.

None of these methods tells us anything about the detailed arrangement in space of the atoms inside the molecule. For this it is necessary to use X-ray diffraction. The average distance between bonded atoms in an organic molecule is about 1½ Angstroms; between unbonded atoms, three to four Angstroms. X-rays have a small enough wavelength (1½ Angstroms) to resolve the atoms, but unfortunately an X-ray diffraction photograph is not a picture in the ordinary sense of the word. We cannot focus X-rays as we can ordinary light; hence a picture can be obtained only by roundabout methods. Moreover, it can show clearly only the periodic, or regularly repeated, parts of the structure.

With patience and skill several English workers have obtained good diffraction pictures of DNA extracted from cells and drawn into long fibers. The first studies, even before details emerged, produced two surprises. First, they revealed that the DNA structure could take two forms. In relatively low humidity, when the water content of the fibers was about 40 per cent, the DNA molecules gave a crystalline pattern, showing that they were aligned regularly in all three dimensions. When the humidity was raised and the fibers took up more water, they increased in length by about 30 per cent and the pattern tended to become "paracrystalline," which means that the molecules were packed side by side in a less regular manner, as if the long molecules could slide over one another somewhat. The second surprising result was that DNA from different species appeared to give identical X-ray patterns, despite the fact that the amounts of the four bases present varied. This was particularly odd because of the existence of the crystalline form just mentioned. How could the structure appear so regular when the bases varied? It seemed that the broad arrangement of the molecule must be independent of the exact sequence of the bases, and it was therefore thought that the bases play no part in holding the structure together. As we shall see, this turned out to be wrong.

The early X-ray pictures showed a third intriguing fact: namely, that the repeats in the crystallographic pattern came at much longer intervals than the chemical repeat units in the molecule. The distance from one phosphate to the next cannot be more than about seven Angstroms, yet the crystallographic repeat came at intervals of 28 Angstroms in the crystalline form and 34 Angstroms in the paracrystalline form; that is, the chemical unit repeated several times before the structure repeated crystallographically.

J. D. Watson and I, working in the Medical Research Council Unit in the Cavendish Laboratory at Cambridge, were convinced that we could get somewhere near the DNA structure by building scale models based on the X-ray patterns obtained by M. H. F. Wilkins, Rosalind Franklin and their co-workers at King's College, London. A great deal is known about the exact distances between bonded atoms in molecules, about the angles between the bonds and about the size of atoms—the so-called van der Waals' distance between adjacent nonbonded atoms. This information is easy to embody in scale models. The problem is rather like a three-dimensional jigsaw puzzle with curious pieces joined together by rotatable joints (single bonds between atoms).

To get anywhere at all we had to make some assumptions. The most important one had to do with the fact that the crystallographic repeat did not coincide with the repetition of chemical units in the chain but came at much longer intervals. A possible explanation was that all the links in the chain were the same but the X-rays were seeing every tenth link, say, from the same angle and the others from different angles. What sort of chain might produce this pattern? The answer was easy: the chain might be coiled in a helix. (A helix is often loosely called a spiral; the distinction is that a helix winds not around a cone but around a cylinder, as a winding staircase usually does.) The distance between crystallographic repeats would then correspond to the distance in the chain between one turn of the helix and the next.

We had some difficulty at first because we ignored the bases and tried to work only with the phosphate-sugar backbone. Eventually we realized that we had to take the bases into account, and this led us quickly to a structure which we now believe to be correct in its broad outlines.

This particular model contains a pair of DNA chains wound around a common axis. The two chains are linked together by their bases. A base on one chain is joined by very weak bonds to a base at the same level on the other chain, and all the bases are paired off in this way right along the structure. In the diagram on page

Structural model shows a pair of DNA chains wound as a double helix around a central axis. The pentose sugars are the white pentagons enclosed in the double line; the phosphate groups are represented by the kink in the double line joining the pentose sugars. From each pentose sugar unit there protrudes a base, shown as a stippled hexagon or pentagon. Each base in turn is linked to an opposing one at the same level by a nitrogen bond. These base-to-base links act as horizontal supports across the axis of the double helix and hold the chains together.

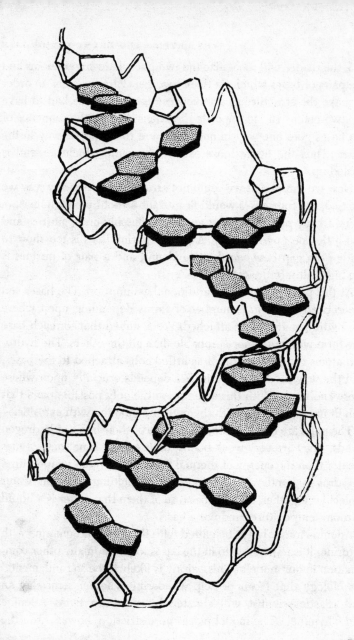

125, the reader will recognize the two phosphate-sugar chains and the pairs of bases which tie them together. Paradoxically, in order to make the structure as symmetrical as possible we had to have the two chains run in opposite directions; that is, the sequence of the bases goes one way in one chain and the opposite way in the other. Thus the figure looks exactly the same whichever end is turned up.

Now we found that we could not arrange the bases any way we pleased; the four bases would fit into the structure only in certain pairs. In any pair there must always be one big one (purine) and one little one (pyrimidine). A pair of pyrimidines is too short to bridge the gap between the two chains, and a pair of purines is too big to fit into the space.

At this point we made an additional assumption. The bases can theoretically exist in a number of forms depending upon where the hydrogen atoms are attached. We assumed that for each base one form was much more probable than all the others. The hydrogen atoms can be thought of as little knobs attached to the bases, and the way the bases fit together depends crucially upon where these knobs are. With this assumption the only possible pairs that will fit in are: adenine with thymine and guanine with cytosine.

The pairs are formed through linkage of their bases of hydrogen bonds. They are very weak bonds; their energy is not many times greater than the energy of thermal vibration at room temperature. (Hydrogen bonds are the main forces holding different water molecules together, and it is because of them that water is a liquid at room temperatures and not a gas.)

Adenine must always be paired with thymine, and guanine with cytosine; it is impossible to fit the bases together in any other combination in our model. (This pairing is likely to be so fundamental for biology that I cannot help wondering whether some day an enthusiastic scientist will christen his newborn twins Adenine and Thymine!) The model places no restriction, however, on the

126

sequence of pairs along the structure. Any specified pair can follow any other. This is because a pair of bases is flat, and since in this model they are stacked roughly like a pile of coins, it does not matter which pair goes above which.

It is important to realize that the specific pairing of the bases is the direct result of the assumption that both phosphate-sugar chains are helical. This regularity implies that the distance from a sugar group on one chain to that on the other at the same level is always the same, no matter where one is along the chain. It follows that the bases linked to the sugars always have the same amount of space in which to fit. It is the regularity of the phosphate-sugar chains, therefore, that is at the root of the specific pairing.

At the moment of writing, detailed interpretation of the X-ray photographs by Wilkins' group at King's College has not been completed, and until this has been done no structure can be considered proved. Nevertheless there are certain features of the model which are so strongly supported by the experimental evidence that it is very likely they will be embodied in the final correct structure. For instance, measurements of the density and water content of the DNA fibers, taken with evidence showing that the fibers can be extended in length, strongly suggest that there are two chains in the structural unit of DNA. Again, recent X-ray pictures have shown clearly a most striking general pattern which we can now recognize as the characteristic signature of a helical structure. In particular there are a large number of places where the diffracted intensity is zero or very small, and these occur exactly where one expects from a helix of this sort. Another feature one would expect is that the X-ray intensities should approach cylindrical symmetry, and it is now known that they do this. Recently Wilkins and his co-workers have given a brilliant analysis of the details of the X-ray pattern of the crystalline form, and have shown that they are consistent with a structure of this type, though in the crystalline form the bases are tilted away from the fiber axis instead of perpendicular, as in our model. Our construction was based on the paracrystalline form.

Many of the physical and chemical properties of DNA can now be understood in terms of this model. For example, the comparative stiffness of the structure explains rather naturally why DNA keeps a long, fiber-like shape in solution. The hydrogen bonds of the bases account for the behavior of DNA in response to changes in pH. Most striking of all is the fact that in every kind of DNA so far examined—and over forty have been analyzed—the amount of adenine is about equal to the amount of thymine and the guanine equal to the cytosine, while the cross-ratios (between, say, adenine and guanine) can vary considerably from species to species. This remarkable fact, first pointed out by Chargaff, is exactly what one would expect according to our model, which requires that every adenine be paired with a thymine and every guanine with a cytosine.

It may legitimately be asked whether the artificially prepared fibers of extracted DNA, on which our model is based, are really representative of intact DNA in the cell. There is every indication that they are. It is difficult to see how the very characteristic features of the model could be produced as artifacts by the extraction process. Moreover, Wilkins has shown that intact biological material, such as sperm heads and bacteriophage, gives X-ray patterns very similar to those of the extracted fibers.

The present position, therefore, is that in all likelihood this statement about DNA can safely be made: its structure consists of two helical chains wound around a common axis and held together by hydrogen bonds between specific pairs of bases.

Replication mechanism by which DNA might duplicate itself is shown in diagram. A helix of two DNA chains unwinds and separates (1). The resulting two complementary chains of DNA within the cell begin to attach DNA precursor units floating loosely (2). When the proper bases are joined, two new helixes will build up (3).

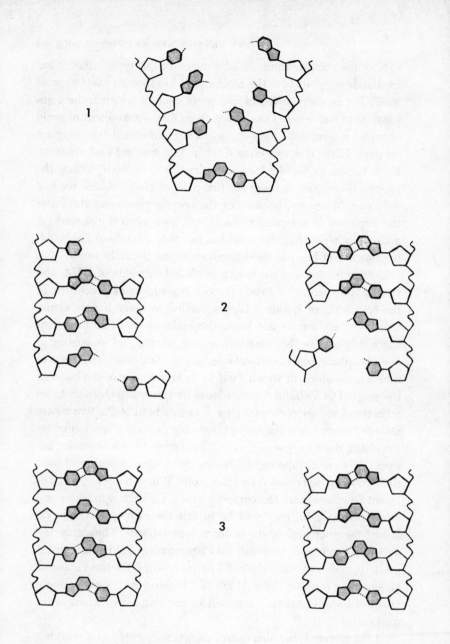

Now the exciting thing about a model of this type is that it immediately suggests how the DNA might produce an exact copy of itself. The model consists of two parts, each of which is the complement of the other. Thus either chain may act as a sort of mold on which a complementary chain can be synthesized (see diagram on page 129). The two chains, let us say, unwind and separate. Each begins to build a new complement onto itself. When the process is completed, there are two pairs of chains where we had only one. Moreover, because of the specific pairing of the bases the sequence of the pairs of bases will have been duplicated exactly; in other words, the mold has not only assembled the building blocks but has put them together in just the right order.

Let us imagine that we have a single helical chain of DNA, and that floating around it inside the cell is a supply of precursors of the four sorts of building blocks needed to make a new chain. Unfortunately we do not know the make-up of these precursor units; they may be, but probably are not, nucleotides, consisting of one phosphate, one sugar and one base. In any case, from time to time a loose unit will attach itself by its base to one of the bases of the single DNA chain. Another loose unit may attach itself to an adjoining base on the chain. Now if one or both of the two newly attached units is not the correct mate for the one it has joined on the chain, the two newcomers will be unable to link together, because they are not the right distance apart. One or both will soon drift away, to be replaced by other units. When, however, two adjacent newcomers are the correct partners for their opposite numbers on the chain, they will be in just the right position to be linked together and begin to form a new chain. Thus only the unit with the proper base will gain a permanent hold at any given position, and eventually the right partners will fill in the vacancies all along the forming chain. While this is going on, the other single chain of the original pair also will be forming a new chain complementary to itself.

At the moment this idea must be regarded simply as a working

130

hypothesis. Not only is there little direct evidence for it, but there are a number of obvious difficulties. For example, certain organisms contain small amounts of a fifth base, 5-methyl cytosine. So far as the model is concerned, 5-methyl cytosine fits just as well as cytosine and it may turn out that it does not matter to the organism which is used, but this has yet to be shown.

A more fundamental difficulty is to explain how the two chains of DNA are unwound in the first place. There would have to be a lot of untwisting, for the total length of all the DNA in a single chromosome is something like four centimeters (400 million Angstroms). This means that there must be more than 10 million turns in all, though the DNA may not be all in one piece.

The duplicating process can be made to appear more plausible by assuming that the synthesis of the two new chains begins as soon as the two original chains start to unwind, so that only a short stretch of the chain is ever really single. In fact, we may postulate that it is the growth of the two new chains that unwinds the original pair. This is likely in terms of energy because, for every hydrogen bond that has to be broken, two new ones will be forming. Moreover, plausibility is added to the idea by the fact that the paired chain forms a rather stiff structure, so that the growing chain would tend to unwind the old pair.

The difficulty of untwisting the two chains is a topological one, and is due to the fact that they are intertwined. There would be no difficulty in "unwinding" a single helical chain, because there are so many single bonds in the chain about which rotation is possible. If in the twin structure one chain should break, the other one could easily spin around. This might relieve accumulated strain, and then the two ends of the broken chain, still being in close proximity, might be joined together again. There is even some evidence suggesting that in the process of extraction the chains of DNA may be broken in quite a number of places and that the structure nevertheless holds together by means of the hydrogen bonding, because there is never a break in both chains

at the same level. Nevertheless, in spite of these tentative suggestions, the difficulty of untwisting remains a formidable one.

There remains the fundamental puzzle as to how DNA exerts
its hereditary influence. A genetic material must carry out two
jobs: duplicate itself and control the development of the rest of
the cell in a specific way. We have seen how it might do the first
of these, but the structure gives no obvious clue concerning how it
may carry out the second. We suspect that the sequence of the
bases acts as a kind of genetic code. Such an arrangement can
carry an enormous amount of information. If we imagine that the
pairs of bases correspond to the dots and dashes of the Morse
code, there is enough DNA in a single cell of the human body to
encode about 1,000 large textbooks. What we want to know, however, is just how this is done in terms of atoms and molecules. In
particular, what precisely is it a code for? As we have seen, the
three key components of living matter—protein, RNA and DNA—
are probably all based on the same general plan. Their backbones
are regular, and the variety comes from the sequence of the side
groups. It is therefore very natural to suggest that the sequence
of the bases of the DNA is in some way a code for the sequence
of the amino acids in the polypeptide chains of the proteins which
the cell must produce. The physicist George Gamow has recently
suggested in a rather abstract way how this information might be
transmitted, but there are some difficulties with the actual scheme
he has proposed, and so far he has not shown how the idea can be
translated into precise molecular configurations.

What then, one may reasonably ask, are the virtues of the proposed model, if any? The prime virtue is that the configuration
suggested is not vague but can be described in terms acceptable
to a chemist. The pairing of the bases can be described rather
exactly. The precise positions of the atoms of the backbone is less
certain, but they can be fixed within limits, and detailed studies
of the X-ray data, now in progress at King's College, may narrow
these limits considerably. Then the structure brings together two

striking pieces of evidence which at first sight seem to be un-related—the analytical data, showing the one-to-one ratios for adenine-thymine and guanine-cytosine, and the helical nature of the X-ray pattern. These can now be seen to be two facets of the same thing. Finally, is it not perhaps a remarkable coincidence, to say the least, to find in this key material a structure of exactly the type one would need to carry out a specific replication process; namely, one showing both variety and complementarity?

The model is also attractive in its simplicity. While it is obvious that whole chromosomes have a fairly complicated structure, it is not unreasonable to hope that the molecular basis underlying them may be rather simple. If this is so, it may not prove too diffi-cult to devise experiments to unravel it. It would, of course, help enormously if biochemists could discover the immediate precursors of DNA. If we knew the monomers from which nature makes DNA, RNA and protein, we might be able to carry out very spec-tacular experiments in the test tube. Be that as it may, we now have for the first time a well-defined model for DNA and for a possible replication process, and this in itself should make it easier to devise crucial experiments.

THE REPRODUCTION OF VIRUSES

by Gunther S. Stent

THE PROCESS of heredity—how like begets like—is one of the most fascinating mysteries in biology, and all over the world biologists are investigating it with enthusiasm and ingenuity. Of the many angles from which they are attacking the problem, none is more exciting than the experiments on bacterial viruses. Here is an organism that reproduces its own kind in a simple and dramatic way. A virus attaches itself to a bacterium and quickly slips inside. Twenty-four minutes later the bacterium pops open like a burst balloon, and out come about 200 new viruses, each an exact copy of the original invader. What is the trick by which the virus manages to make all these living replicas of itself from the hodgepodge of materials at hand? What happens in the host cell in those critical 24 minutes?

Within the past few years studies with radioactive tracers have made it possible to begin to answer these questions. By labeling with radioactive atoms the substances of the virus or of the medium in which it multiplies, experimenters can follow these materials and trace the events that lead to the construction of a new virus. This article will tell about some of the experiments and the facts learned from them.

The bacterial virus, a tiny organism only seven-millionths of an inch long, is a nucleoprotein: that is, a particle made up half of protein and half of nucleic acid. The latter is desoxyribonucleic acid—the well-known DNA which is a basic stuff of all cell nuclei. The role of DNA was considered at some length by A. E. Mirsky in his discussion of chromosome chemistry in an earlier chapter. We are interested in the respective roles of the two parts of the virus molecule: the protein and the DNA. We are also interested in where the various materials come from when a virus synthesizes replicas of itself inside the bacteria growing in a culture medium.

First let us consider the tracer technique. Suppose we wish to label the DNA part of the virus particles. Since an important constituent of DNA is its phosphate links, we shall label the element phosphorus with the radioactive isotope phosphorus 32. We begin with the medium in which we are growing bacteria that are to be infected by the virus. The culture contains inorganic phosphate as the source of phosphorus for the bacteria. To this medium we add a little radiophosphorus, so that there is one radioactive atom for every billion atoms of ordinary, nonradioactive phosphorus. The bacteria will take up the same proportion of radioactive and ordinary phosphorus. We can tell how much phosphate the bacteria contain simply by counting the radiophosphorus atoms with a Geiger counter: the total amount of phosphorus is a billion times that.

Now if we infect the culture of bacteria with viruses, the virus progeny also will have the same proportion of radiophosphorus. But to measure their phosphorus we must isolate them, for the culture contains a great deal of phosphorus not incorporated in them. We can separate the viruses in three ways: (1) by a series of centrifuging operations that remove the other materials through their differences in weight; (2) by adding nonradioactive bacteria, on which the viruses become fixed and which can then be removed by low-speed centrifugation; or (3) by adding a serum (developed in rabbits) which contains antibodies that combine with the viruses and precipitate them from the culture.

Two radioactive isotopes are used in the bacterial virus work: phosphorus 32 to label phosphate and the DNA part of the virus, sulfur 35 to label the protein part of the virus. Now let us look at the experiments.

All of these experiments were done on bacterial viruses of the strain called T2, which infects the common bacterium *Escherichia coli.* Some years ago two investigators—Thomas F. Anderson of the University of Pennsylvania and Roger M. Herriott of the Johns Hopkins University—observed that something curious happened to bacterial viruses when they were exposed to "osmotic shock," namely, a sudden change in osmotic pressure effected by adding distilled water to the liquid in which they were suspended. These viruses could still attack and kill bacteria. But they had lost their ability to reproduce. Under the electron microscope they looked like sacs that had been emptied of their contents, and a chemical analysis indicated that they had lost all their DNA.

Recently A. D. Hershey and M. W. Chase, working at the Carnegie Institution of Washington genetics laboratory in Cold Spring Harbor, N. Y., repeated and confirmed these experiments with the help of radioactive tracers. The DNA, labeled with radiophosphorus, was indeed removed from the virus by osmotic shock. It remained as DNA in the solution, but it was easily broken down by an enzyme—an indication that it had lost the protection of the protein "coat" of the virus. As for the protein shell of the virus, when separated from the solution and placed in a culture of bac-

Reproduction of bacterial viruses is shown in four stages; clock indicates progress and approximate time of the reaction. The large stippled object is the bacterium. Virus is shown in two parts: its outer layer is the protein which has the ability to attach itself to the surface of the bacterium and to react with antivirus serum; its core (*black*) is the nucleic acid. First stage of reproduction is infection. In it the virus particle attaches itself, probably by the tail, to the bacterium, and the nucleic acid core empties into bacterial cell, the protein coat remaining outside. In the second stage, the "dark" period, the virus nucleic acid within the bacterial cell has begun to induce the formation of new protein coats. However, the coats contain no nucleic acid and there are as yet no infective particles, not even the particle that caused the original infection. In the third phase, called the "rise period", some of the protein coats contain nucleic acid; they are the first infective particles of the new generation. The final stage occurs about 30 minutes after the first. The infected bacterium bursts and releases the new generation of virus particles into the surrounding medium. Only a few of the 200 particles in the new generation of bacterial viruses are depicted.

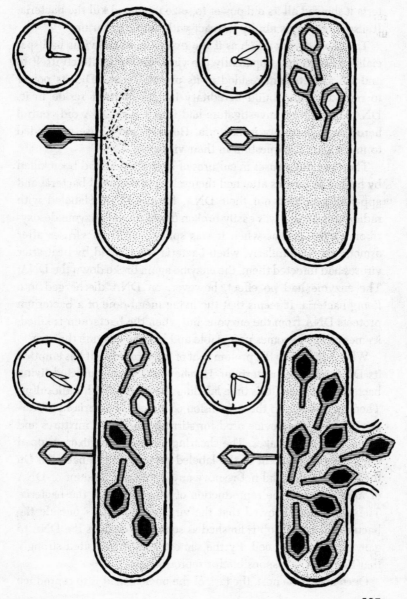

teria it showed all its old power to seize upon and kill the bacteria. It also retained its ability to react with antivirus serum.

This looked very much as if the two parts of the virus had specialized functions. Apparently the virus' ability to attach itself to and kill a bacterium resided in its protein "coat." Did its power to reproduce and build hereditary images of itself reside in its DNA core? Other investigators had found that DNA did control hereditary continuity in bacteria. Hershey and Chase proceeded to investigate the question in their viruses.

They first put viruses in cultures of bacteria that had been killed by heat. The viruses attached themselves to the dead bacteria and apparently poured out their DNA, for the DNA (labeled with radiophosphorus) was easily broken down by the enzyme desoxyribonuclease, just as when it was spilled out from viruses after osmotic shock. Similarly, when bacteria were killed by heat after viruses had infected them, the enzyme again broke down the DNA. The enzyme had no effect, however, on DNA discharged into *living* bacteria. It seems that the living membrane of a bacterium protects DNA from the enzyme, but when the bacterium is killed, its membrane becomes permeable and lets the enzyme through.

What happens to the protein coat of the virus after it has emptied its DNA into the bacterium? Hershey and Chase infected living bacteria with virus, this time labeling the protein with radiosulfur. Then they shook up the suspension of infected bacteria in a Waring Blendor—the device used for stirring laboratory mixtures and for making milk shakes. The shearing force of the mixer stripped more than 80 per cent of the labeled protein off the bacteria. On the other hand, it did not remove any significant amount of DNA or interfere with the reproduction of viruses within the bacteria. The experiment showed that the virus protein stays outside the bacterium, and its job is finished as soon as it enables the DNA to gain entry into the cell. By the same token, it indicated strongly that the DNA is responsible for reproduction.

Once inside the host, the task of the nucleic acid is to reproduce

138

itself 200-fold. It must also stimulate the production of 200 protein coats exactly like the one it has just shed. Where do the raw materials come from, and how are they put together?

In 1946 Seymour S. Cohen of the University of Pennsylvania, the first investigator to study bacterial virus reproduction with radioactive tracers, conceived an experiment directed to this question. He wished to find out whether the needed raw materials, particularly the phosphorus, came from the bacterial cell itself or from the medium surrounding it. He grew two cultures of bacteria, one in a medium containing radiophosphorus, the other in a nonradioactive medium. Then he removed the bacterial cells from the liquid in the two test tubes and switched them, putting the nonradioactive bacteria in the radioactive medium and vice versa. Now he infected both cultures with viruses. When the bacteria burst and the new viruses emerged, he isolated the viruses and measured their radioactivity. The viruses that came out of the nonradioactive bacteria transferred to the radioactive medium were radioactive: they had two thirds as high a concentration of radiophosphorus as the medium in which the bacteria had been immersed. On the other hand, the viruses that came from the radioactive bacteria in the nonradioactive medium had only one third as much radiophosphorus as the bacteria. Cohen therefore concluded that the new generations of viruses had obtained two thirds of their phosphorus from the growth medium while they were being formed and only one third from their host bacteria. This was a great surprise to those bacteriologists who had long supposed that bacterial viruses were formed from ready-made structures already present in the host cell.

At the University of Chicago Frank W. Putnam and Lloyd M. Kozloff, making similar studies with nitrogen 15 as the tracer, have found that the protein of viruses, like their DNA, is derived mostly from substances assimilated from the growth medium.

Cohen's experiment had covered the state of the system at just one stage: the next step was to follow the whole history of the conversion of inorganic phosphorus into virus DNA, from the moment bacteria began to grow in the medium until the newborn viruses finally emerged. At the State Serum Institute of Denmark, Ole Maaloe and I extended Cohen's experiment with radiophosphorus, making the switch of radioactive bacteria to a nonradioactive medium and vice versa at many different stages in the development of the culture, both before and after infection of the bacteria with virus. In this way we were able to determine just how much of the phosphorus that the bacteria eventually donated to the new viruses was assimilated by them from the medium during the various periods of development. Before they were infected with virus, the bacteria took up that phosphorus at the rate of their own growth, which means that they were using the phosphorus to make their own DNA. But after infection, their assimilation of phosphorus that they were to donate to the viruses increased sharply. Most of the phosphorus the bacteria were now taking up was going directly into the synthesis of new viruses.

We also observed that it takes at least 12 minutes to convert inorganic phosphorus into virus DNA. Hence any phosphorus that is to go into the making of the new viruses must have been assimilated by the bacteria by the end of the first 12 minutes of the 24-minute period during which the viruses are synthesized in the cell. As a matter of fact, A. H. Doermann has found that the 24-minute latent period divides into two 12-minute phases. In experiments at Cold Spring Harbor he opened infected bacteria at various stages. During the first half of the latent period there were no fully formed viruses with infective power within the bacterial cell; even the original invader had disappeared. Then, after 12 minutes, the first infective particle appeared, and more followed until there were 200 just before the cell burst. The explanation is clear. The original invading virus had shed its protein coat on entering the cell and therefore was no longer an infective unit. No virus could appear in the cell until at least one new protein coat had been manufactured and coupled with a unit of DNA. Apparently this proceeding takes some 12 minutes.

It seems that the manufacture of protein and of DNA goes on side by side within the cell. In experiments with radiosulfur as the label, Maaloe and Neville Symonds of the California Institute of Technology have recently shown that by the time the first new infective virus appears, there is already enough virus protein in the cell to form about 60 viruses. On the other hand, in similar experiments with radiophosphorus as the label we have found indications that completed units of DNA do not unite with protein units until the last moment; the particle then becomes infective.

The DNA of the original invading virus is responsible, as we have seen, for reproduction within the cell, both of DNA itself and of protein. How does it go about its job? Putnam and Kozloff labeled viruses with radiophosphorus and followed the radioactivity to see what happened to the phosphorus after the viruses infected bacteria. They found that about 40 per cent of the labeled phosphorus showed up in the viruses' progeny, the rest being discarded in the debris. Experiments with radiocarbon have shown that the same is true of other constituents of the DNA. In other words, about 40 per cent of the DNA of the parent viruses is passed on to the descendants.

How is the old DNA passed on? Is the parent's DNA handed on intact to a single individual virus offspring in each bacterial cell in a random 40 per cent of the cases, or is it distributed generally among the descendants? At Washington University in St. Louis, Hershey, Martin D. Kamen, Howard Gest and J. W. Kennedy examined this question. They infected bacteria in a highly radioactive medium (one in every 1,000 phosphorus atoms was radioactive) with nonradioactive viruses. The DNA of the parent viruses was stable; not containing any radiophosphorus, it would not decay by radioactivity. Hence if it was passed on intact, a recognizable number of the viruses' descendants also should have stable DNA. But this was not the case. The descendant population steadily lost its infectivity, due to radioactive decay of its phosphorus atoms, until fewer than one tenth of 1 per cent of the descendants were infective.

Is it possible that the hereditary continuity of the virus resides in a fraction consisting of 40 per cent of the DNA, and that the rest of the DNA does not participate in reproduction at all? To answer this question Maaloe and James D. Watson at the State Serum Institute of Denmark produced three generations of virus. The first had its DNA labeled with radiophosphorus. A single virus of this generation then produced generation II, and passed on to it 40 per cent of its radiophosphorus. Now if the radiophosphorus transmitted from generation I to generation II was carried in a special reproductive fraction of the DNA, all of it should have been passed on to generation III. Actually it was found that generation III received only the usual 40 per cent. One must therefore conclude that the parent DNA material is not handed on in intact fractions but rather is distributed in a general fashion over the structures of the descendants.

Summing up, the tracer studies so far have given us the following picture of how bacterial viruses reproduce themselves. By means of some property residing in its protein coat, a virus is able to attach itself to the surface of a bacterial cell. The contact immediately uncorks the virus, and it pours its DNA into the cell. The emptied protein coat is left outside the cell and thereafter plays no further part. Inside the cell the virus DNA begins to make replicas of itself, using as raw materials the nucleic acids of the bacterium and fresh substances absorbed by the bacterium from the medium surrounding it. About 40 per cent of the parent virus DNA itself is conserved and will reappear in the descendants. The virus DNA also induces the synthesis of new protein in the cell. Finally units of the protein combine with DNA replicas to form 200 exact copies of the parent virus.

The facts discovered so far give us only an outline of the process, but they seem a good start on the road to solving the mystery of how organisms build structural copies of themselves and pass on their heredity from generation to generation.

RICKETTSIAE

by Marianna Bovarnick

RICKETTSIAE are of interest not only as a major cause of human disease but also as a new kind of organism for biologists to study. They are in the realm of life between the bacteria and the viruses: like viruses they are parasites that can multiply only within a living host cell, but in size, complexity and metabolic powers they approach the free-living bacteria. Where do they fit into the scheme of evolution? Can they tell us anything about the origin of viruses and of bacteria?

One rickettsial disease, epidemic typhus, has been for centuries a great scourge of mankind. It has been closely associated with wars and the attendant human wretchedness, as attested by some of its names—jail fever, camp fever, hospital fever. The disease was first recognized during the fifteenth-century wars of Granada in Spain. Afterward it swept over the entire continent of Europe. Hans Zinsser credits epidemic typhus with determining the outcome of at least one war: in the sixteenth century it defeated the attempt of Francis I to wrest Italy and the papal power from the grasp of Charles V, ruler of Spain. During the wars of succeeding centuries, typhus frequently killed more people than actual combat. As recently as World War I it wrought havoc in parts of eastern Europe; immediately after that war it afflicted some thirty million in Russia and killed three million. During World War II outbreaks of typhus occurred in the Mediterranean area, in German prison camps and in the Far East; there was a severe epidemic of some 26,000 cases shortly after the war in Japan and Korea. But the disease is so well understood today that it need no longer take any such toll of death as in the past.

Besides epidemic typhus the rickettsial diseases include Rocky Mountain spotted fever, scrub typhus and murine typhus. All of these diseases are characterized by a rash and a fever. Scrub typhus, or tsutsugamushi disease, found in Japan and other parts of the Pacific, created a considerable military problem during World War II until methods were worked out for its prevention and treatment. Murine typhus, which occurs in many parts of the world including the U. S., is comparatively mild but closely related to epidemic typhus; an attack by one confers immunity after recovery against both.

The infectious rickettsia is transmitted by an insect carrier. The first to discover this was the French bacteriologist Charles Nicolle, who found that epidemic typhus was carried from person to person by the louse. Not long afterward it was demonstrated that Rocky Mountain spotted fever was transmitted to man by ticks, which are not only the carriers but also the natural reservoir of the microorganism. The natural hosts of scrub typhus and murine typhus proved to be rats and field mice; scrub typhus is carried to man by mites and murine typhus by the rat louse.

The discovery that lice transmit epidemic typhus made it easy to understand why the disease spread like wildfire in times when everyone from the highest to the lowest wore one set of clothing day and night without change all winter. But it was not so easy to understand why the disease persisted from one great epidemic to another in the absence of any apparent reservoir. Since the infection is inevitably fatal for the louse, one would suppose that the disease should disappear after an epidemic had subsided and the infected lice had died off. What was the reservoir that preserved the infective agent? This puzzle was solved after Dr. Nathan E. Brill of New York City observed sporadic cases of a relatively mild disease similar to typhus in patients who had had no recent contact with lice. Epidemic typhus had never been found in New York. Zinsser, studying the records, noted that most of the patients with Brill's disease, as it came to be known, were immigrants from

144

eastern Europe. He suggested that they may have had attacks of epidemic typhus in the old country and that the disease may have returned because the patients had preserved the rickettsiae in some quiescent state in their own tissues. Recent studies by E. S. Murray and J. C. Snyder have shown that lice fed upon such patients become infected by rickettsiae indistinguishable from epidemic typhus strains.

The rickettsiae themselves were identified early in this century. The epidemic typhus organism was seen under the microscope in stained smears of the intestines of infected lice. It was called *Rickettsiae prowazeki* in honor of the first two investigators who described it, Howard T. Ricketts and Stanislas von Prowazek, both of whom died of typhus contracted during their studies.

Preventive vaccines against rickettsial diseases were eventually prepared, at first from infected lice and later from cultures of rickettsiae grown in the yolk sacs of chick embryos. These vaccines, consisting of killed organisms, reduce the mortality from rickettsial infections practically to zero. Moreover, there are now several antibiotics—aureomycin, chloramphenicol and terramycin—which are extremely effective against the rickettsial diseases.

Interest is now concentrated on the nature and behavior of the organisms. Several methods for quantitative assay of their multiplication and virulence in animals have been developed. These usually take longer than similar work with viruses or bacteria, because the rickettsiae grow rather slowly. There is one rapid method, however, in the case of the typhus strains. Injection of a high concentration of typhus rickettsiae into the tail vein of a mouse kills the animal within a few hours. Apparently the quick death is due not to overwhelming multiplication of the rickettsiae, but to a toxin. This toxin has so far defied isolation from the organisms, but its existence has been virtually demonstrated by the fact that biological inactivation of the rickettsiae by ultraviolet irradiation does not reduce their toxicity to the mice.

One important issue in biology on which the rickettsiae may

shed light is this: Are viruses aberrant derivatives from cells or are they degenerate end-products of an evolution from some higher form? According to the first theory, the viruses originally evolved from some portion of living host cells, perhaps the genes. According to the second, they evolved from more complex microorganisms, perhaps bacteria; in the process they lost all the metabolic abilities of bacteria and became completely dependent upon the cells they invade for all the reactions and chemical syntheses necessary for their reproduction. Now in rickettsiae we seem to have a link between viruses and bacteria: like the viruses they can grow only in living cells, but they also appear to have some of the metabolic capabilities of bacteria.

To investigate the metabolic activities of rickettsiae we had to find a way of keeping these highly unstable organisms alive and active outside their host cells. Our study of the factors affecting the stability of typhus rickettsiae led to the discovery of several interesting facts concerning their biochemical capability.

In these experiments rickettsiae were incubated for a specified time at 93 degrees Fahrenheit in various nutrient solutions and then assayed for the relative numbers remaining. In a nutrient broth in which bacteria thrive, the rickettsiae lost all activity within a few hours. But they survived moderately well for several hours in relatively simple salt solutions similar to the fluids in the cells of an animal's body. The first studies also disclosed that the vitality of rickettsiae, as measured by their infectivity, was markedly increased if glutamic acid, an amino acid, was added to the salt solution. Follow-up tests soon showed that the organisms could metabolize glutamic acid. They also proved capable of oxidizing slowly two other substances, pyruvate and succinate, which, like glutamic acid, are oxidized by most animal and plant tissues. Of many substances tried, these three were the only ones typhus rickettsiae could utilize in any significant amount. However, W. H. Price of The Johns Hopkins University School of Hygiene and Public Health has recently found that spotted fever rickettsiae can oxidize three other substances: ketoglutarate, fumarate and oxalo-acetate.

All of these compounds are participants in the well-known citric acid cycle of reactions. This cycle is carried out by mitochondria, small particles in the cells of animals. In the final stages of the cycle the mitochondria take up inorganic phosphate to form the energy-rich compound adenosine triphosphate (ATP), which supplies the energy for many activities of animal cells. Now there are indications that the entire citric acid cycle may also take place in rickettsiae. For example, their oxidation of glutamic acid is dependent on the presence of inorganic phosphate, although it has not been possible to show that they convert the inorganic phosphate to ATP during these oxidations. The difficulty in these investigations lies mainly in the fact that no one has yet succeeded in preparing active extracts of rickettsiae that retain their enzymatic activity.

The similarity of rickettsiae to mitochondria emerged in another highly interesting series of experiments. We tested the behavior of the organisms toward coenzymes, the smaller partners whose co-operation many enzymes require to carry out their functions as catalysts. It turned out that the rickettsiae very definitely used the coenzymes known as DPN (diphosphopyridine nucleotide) and coenzyme A, both of which are essential for many oxidation reactions in animal cells. In further experiments it also developed that these two coenzymes had a remarkable ability to restore rickettsiae that had been inactivated by freezing to minus 94 degrees Fahrenheit. Ordinarily such rickettsiae, when thawed, show a loss of nearly all their infectivity. But when incubated with DPN and coenzyme A for a few hours at 93 degrees F., they regained a large proportion of the original activity; the gain often amounted to as much as 10-fold.

The most probable explanation was that the rickettsiae normally contain these coenzymes but lose them through the cell membrane when the membrane is damaged by freezing. Further experiments

147

involving analysis of extracts of the rickettsiae for DPN showed that this was indeed the case.

That rickettsiae should require DPN for oxidation was not surprising, since it is necessary for so many oxidative reactions in other cells. That the organisms' infectivity also should depend upon the presence of DPN did seem surprising, because any host cell could supply them with that substance. Possibly the explanation is that rickettsiae need DPN to penetrate into the host cells.

A quite different type of reversible change has been observed in spotted fever rickettsiae. Ticks infected with a virulent strain of this rickettsia usually kill from 25 to 50 per cent of guinea pigs into which they are inoculated. The rickettsiae lose this lethal power if the infected ticks are kept for several months in a refrigerator, though guinea pigs inoculated with them do become immune. However, the refrigerated organisms regain the ability to produce severe disease in guinea pigs if they are warmed for several days at 93 degrees F. Price has recently shown experimentally that refrigerated rickettsiae retain their infectivity for eggs while they lack infectivity for guinea pigs.

These findings recall the cases of the patients with Brill's disease, who apparently harbored quiescent typhus rickettsiae in their tissues for years. It is tempting to speculate that, just as the loss of DPN deprives the rickettsia of all activity, the loss of some other substance may strip it of part of its capacities, such as the ability to penetrate or to multiply in some of its usual host cells.

From the microbiologist's point of view the most interesting fact is that mitochondria show the same elements of behavior as rickettsiae on freezing. Mitochondria that have been frozen in a salt medium no longer can carry on their usual oxidations. Addition of DPN restores at least a part of their original activity, and it has been shown that they also normally contain bound DPN, which escapes on freezing. Moreover, both rickettsiae and mitochondria can be protected against loss of their activity by the addition of sucrose to the liquid in which they are frozen.

The similarity between mitochondria and rickettsiae, both in their biochemistry and in their appearance, suggests that the rickettsiae might have evolved from the mitochondria. But this seems doubtful. It is known that the rickettsiae contain desoxyribonucleic acid, which is not found in the mitochondria. The mitochondria can oxidize many substances, in particular fatty acids, which typhus rickettsiae apparently cannot.

If rickettsiae evolved from mitochondria, and viruses from genes, there should be sharp lines of demarcation between bacteria, rickettsiae and viruses, corresponding to the distinctions that exist between cells, mitochondria and genes. The contrary is the fact: there appears to be a continuous gradation in size and chemical complexity from the smallest through the largest viruses and on through the rickettsiae and the bacteria. The bacteria themselves have a wide spectrum of growth requirements, ranging from just inorganic salts to growth factors even more complex than the higher animals require.

The more attractive hypothesis is that first the rickettsiae, then the viruses, evolved gradually from the bacteria by increasing loss of the enzymes necessary for functions rendered superfluous by development of a parasitic mode of existence. As they evolved they borrowed more and more of the enzymatic apparatus of their host cells, until for many viruses the host cell appears to provide all of the reactions for multiplication.

The chief distinctions between rickettsiae and bacteria are far from completely clear cut. Some organisms fully as complex as the bacteria, such as the malaria parasites, can grow only in living cells. On the other hand, at least one virus, the influenza virus, can carry out a chemical reaction: it catalyzes a cleavage of a complex compound in the membrane of the cells that it invades. It seems probable to the author that the distinctions between bacteria, rickettsiae and viruses as types of organisms may disappear as more is learned about them; that some of the reactions which take place in rickettsiae may be found in the large viruses, and that it may prove possible to grow rickettsiae outside a living cell by supplying them with the necessary complex molecules.

PART 4 ENZYMES AND ENERGY

I. THE GENES OF MEN AND MOLDS
by George Beadle

Head of the California Institute of Technology Division of Biology, George Beadle is a geneticist, whose most notable work has been done with the bread mold *Neurospora,* the subject of this chapter. With the great Caltech chemist Linus Pauling, he is engaged in a famous research partnership on the fundamental problems of biology and medicine. To house this enterprise, a $3,000,000 laboratory is now under construction on the campus at Pasadena. Since he is also president, this year, of the American Association for the Advancement of Science, Beadle is finding little time for the daring sport of rock climbing which he took up at a time in life when most athletes become spectators.

II. ENZYMES
by John Pfeiffer

A science journalist, not a scientist, John Pfeiffer has been science editor of *Newsweek,* science director of the Columbia Broadcasting System, a member of the staff of SCIENTIFIC AMERICAN and now is engaged in free-lance writing. Pfeiffer is author of *The Human Brain* (Harper & Bros., 1955) and, on a Guggenheim fellowship, is writing a book on modern astronomy.

III. THE METABOLISM OF FATS
by David E. Green

A pioneer among U. S. workers in the comparatively young field of enzyme chemistry, David E. Green graduated from the University of the State of New York in 1930. He secured his graduate training in England where he worked until 1941, as a Breit Foundation research fellow. Upon his return to the U. S., he took charge of the enzyme research laboratory of the College of Physicians and Surgeons at Columbia University. He is now a professor of enzyme chemistry and does research at the Institute for Enzyme Research at the University of Wisconsin.

THE GENES OF MEN AND MOLDS

by George Beadle

Eighty-five years ago, in the garden of a monastery near the village of Brünn in what is now Czechoslovakia, Gregor Johann Mendel was spending his spare moments studying hybrids between varieties of the edible garden pea. Out of his penetrating analysis of the results of his studies there grew the modern theory of the gene. But like many a pioneer in science, Mendel was a generation ahead of his time; the full significance of his findings was not appreciated until 1900.

In the period following the "rediscovery" of Mendel's work biologists have developed and extended the gene theory to the point where it now seems clear that genes are the basic units of all living things. They are the master molecules that guide the development and direct the vital activities of men and amoebas.

Today the specific functions of genes in plants and animals are being isolated and studied in detail. One of the most useful genetic guinea pigs is the red bread mold *Neurospora crassa*. Its genes can conveniently be changed artificially and the part that they play in the chemical alteration and metabolism of cells can be analyzed with considerable precision. We are learning what sort of material the genes are made of, how they affect living organisms and how the genes themselves, and thereby heredity, are affected by forces in their environment. Indeed, in their study of genes biologists are coming closer to an understanding of the ultimate basis of life itself.

It seems likely that life first appeared on earth in the form of units much like the genes of present-day organisms. Through the processes of mutation in such primitive genes, and through Darwinian natural selection, higher forms of life evolved—first as simple systems with a few genes, then as single-celled forms with many genes, and finally as multicellular plants and animals in which genes are arranged linearly in the threadlike chromosomes of the cell nuclei.

What do we know about these genes that are so all-important in the process of evolution, in the development of complex organisms, and in the direction of those vital processes which distinguish the living from the nonliving worlds? Genes are characterized by students of heredity as the units of inheritance. What is meant by this may be illustrated by examples of some inherited traits in man.

Blue-eyed people may differ by a single gene from those with brown eyes. This eye-color gene exists in two forms, which for convenience may be designated B (for brown) and b (for blue).

Every person begins as a single cell a few thousandths of an inch in diameter—a cell that comes into being through the fusion of an egg cell from the mother and a sperm cell from the father. This fertilized egg carries two representatives of the eye-color gene, one from each parent. Depending on the parents, there are therefore three types of individuals possible so far as this particular gene is concerned. They start from fertilized eggs represented by the genetic formulas BB, Bb, and bb. The first two types, BB and Bb, will develop into individuals with brown eyes. The third one, bb, will have blue eyes. You will note that when both forms of the gene are present the individual is brown-eyed. This is because the form of the gene for brown eyes is *dominant* over its alternative form for blue eyes. Conversely, the form for blue eyes is said to be *recessive*.

During the division of the fertilized egg cell into many daughter cells, which through growth, division and specialization give rise to a fully developed person, the genes multiply regularly with each cell division. As a result each of the millions of cells of a fully developed individual carries exact copies of the two representatives of the eye-color gene which has been contributed by the parents.

152

In the formation of egg and sperm cells, the genes are again reduced from two to one per cell. Therefore a mother of the type *BB* forms egg cells carrying only the *B* form of the gene. A type *bb* mother produces only *b* egg cells. A *Bb* mother, on the other hand, produces both *B* and *b* egg cells, in equal numbers on the average. Exactly corresponding relations hold for the formation of sperm cells.

With these facts in mind it is a simple matter to determine the types of children expected to result from various unions. Some of these are indicated in the following list:

Mother	Father	Children
BB (brown)	*BB* (brown)	All *BB* (brown)
Bb (brown)	*Bb* (brown)	¼ *BB* (brown)
		½ *Bb* (brown)
		¼ *bb* (blue)
BB (brown)	*bb* (blue)	All *Bb* (brown)
Bb (brown)	*bb* (blue)	½ *Bb* (brown)
		½ *bb* (blue)
bb (blue)	*bb* (blue)	All *bb* (blue)

This table shows that while it is expected that some families in which both parents have brown eyes will include blue-eyed children, parents who are both blue-eyed are not expected to have brown-eyed children.

It is important to emphasize conditions that may account for apparent exceptions to the last rule. The first is that eye-color inheritance in man is not completely worked out genetically. Probably other genes besides the one used as an example here are concerned with eye color. It may therefore be possible, when these other genes are taken into account, for parents with true blue eyes to have brown-eyed children. A second factor which accounts for some apparent exceptions is that brown-eyed persons of the *Bb* type may have eyes so light brown that an inexperienced

153

observer may classify them as blue. Two parents of this type may, of course, have a *BB* child with dark brown eyes.

Another example of an inherited trait in man is curly hair. Ordinary curly hair, such as is found frequently in people of European descent, is dominant to straight hair. Therefore parents with curly hair may have straight-haired children but straight-haired parents do not often have children with curly hair. Again there are other genes concerned, and the simple rules based on a one-gene interpretation do not always hold.

Eye-color and hair-form genes have relatively trivial effects in human beings. Other known genes are concerned with traits of deeper significance. One of these involves a rare hereditary disease in which the principal symptom is urine that turns black on exposure to air. This "inborn error of metabolism," as the English physician and biochemist Sir Archibald Garrod referred to it, has been known to medical men for probably 300 years. Its biochemical basis was established in 1859 by the German biochemist C. Bödeker, who showed that darkening of urine is due to a specific chemical substance called alcapton, later identified chemically as 2,5-dihydroxyphenylacetic acid. The disease is known as alcaptonuria, meaning "alcapton in the urine."

Alcaptonuria is known to result from a gene defect. It shows typical Mendelian inheritance, like blue eyes, but the defective form of the gene is much less frequent in the population than is the recessive form of the eye-color gene.

The excretion of alcapton is a result of the body's inability to break it down by oxidation. Normal individuals possess an enzyme which makes possible a reaction by which alcapton is further oxidized. This enzyme is absent in alcaptonurics. As a result alcaptonurics cannot degrade alcapton to carbon dioxide and water as normal individuals do.

Alcaptonuria is of special interest genetically and biochemically because it gives us a clue as to what genes do and how they do it. If the cells of an individual contain only the recessive or inactive form of the gene, no enzyme is formed, alcapton accumulates and is excreted in the urine. The role of the normal form of the gene in enzyme production is thus made clear.

Man, however, is far from an ideal organism in which to study genes. His life cycle is too long, his offspring are too few, his choice of a mate is not often based on a desire to contribute to the knowledge of heredity, and it is inconvenient to subject him to a complete chemical analysis. As a result, most of what we have learned about genes has come from studies of such organisms as garden peas, Indian corn plants and the fruit fly *Drosophila.*

In these and other plants and animals there are many instances in which genes seem to be responsible for specific chemical reactions. It is believed that in most or all of these cases they act as pattern molecules from which enzymes are copied.

Many enzymes have been isolated in a pure crystalline state. All of them have proved to be proteins or to contain proteins as essential parts. Gene-enzymes relations such as those considered above suggest that the primary function of genes may be to serve as models from which specific kinds of enzyme proteins are copied. This hypothesis is strengthened by evidence that some genes control the presence of proteins that are not parts of enzymes.

For example, normal persons have a specific blood protein that is important in blood clotting. Bleeders, known as hemophiliacs, differ from nonbleeders by a single gene. Its normal form is presumed to be essential for the synthesis of the specific blood-clotting protein. Hemophilia, incidentally, is almost completely limited to the male because it is sex-linked; that is, it is carried in the so-called X chromosome, which is concerned with the determination of sex. Many other abnormalities (e.g., color blindness) are sex-linked.

The genes that control blood types in man and other animals direct the production of so-called antigens. These are giant molecules which apparently derive their specificity from gene models, and which are capable of inducing the formation of specific antibodies.

The hypothesis that genes are concerned with the elaboration of giant protein molecules has been tested by experiments with the red mold *Neurospora*. This fungus has many advantages in the study of what genes do. It has a short life cycle—only 10 days from one sexual spore generation to the next. It multiplies profusely by asexual spores. The result is that any strain can be multiplied a million fold in a few days without any genetic change. Each of the cell nuclei that carry the genes of the bread mold has only a single set of genes instead of the two sets found in the cells of man and other higher organisms. This means that recessive genes are not hidden by their dominant counterparts.

During the sexual stage, in which molds of opposite sex reactions come together, there is a union comparable to that between egg and sperm in man. The fusion nucleus then immediately undergoes two divisions in which genes are reduced again to one per cell. The four products formed from a single fusion nucleus by these divisions are lined up in a spore sac. Each divides again so as to produce pairs of nuclei that are genetically identical. The eight resulting nuclei are included in eight sexual spores, each one-thousandth of an inch long. This life cycle of *Neurospora* is shown in the illustration on the opposite page.

Using a microscope, a skilled laboratory worker can dissect the sexual spores from the spore sac in orderly sequence. Each of them

Life cycle of the mold *Neurospora* begins at the top center of this illustration with the hyphal fusion (corresponding to sexual mating in higher forms) of sex a and sex A. The union produces a fertile egg, in which two complete sets of genes are paired. The egg then divides (*center of drawing*), and divides again. This produces four nuclei, each of which has only a single set of genes. Lined up in a spore sac, the four nuclei divide once more to produce four pairs of nuclei, each pair being genetically identical. A group of spore sacs is gathered in a fruiting body. At this point, a skilled worker can dissect each of the sexual spores from the spore sac and plant them separately in culture tubes. Here genetic defects can be exposed by changing the ingredients of the media; here also *Neurospora* will multiply by asexual means, making it possible to grow large quantities of the mold without genetic change.

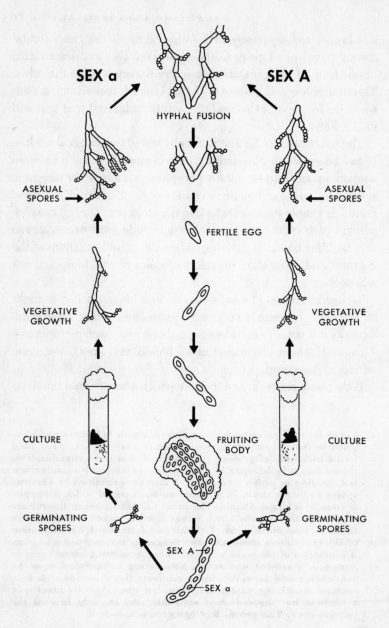

SEX a

SEX A

HYPHAL FUSION

ASEXUAL SPORES

ASEXUAL SPORES

FERTILE EGG

VEGETATIVE GROWTH

VEGETATIVE GROWTH

CULTURE

FRUITING BODY

CULTURE

GERMINATING SPORES

GERMINATING SPORES

SEX A

SEX a

can be planted separately in a culture tube. If the two parental strains differ by a single gene, four spores always carry descendants of one form of the gene and four carry descendants of the other. Thus if a yellow and a white strain are crossed, there occur in each spore sac four spores that will give white molds and four that will give yellow.

The red bread mold is almost ideally suited for chemical studies. It can be grown in pure culture on a chemically known medium containing only nitrate, sulfate, phosphate, various other inorganic substances, sugar and biotin, a vitamin of the B group. From these relatively simple starting materials, the mold produces all the constituent parts of its protoplasm. These include some twenty amino acid building blocks of proteins, nine water-soluble vitamins of the B group, and many other organic molecules of vital biological significance.

To one interested in what genes do in a human being, it might at first thought seem a very large jump from a man to a mold. Actually it is not. For in its basic metabolic processes, protoplasm—Thomas Huxley's physical stuff of life—is very much the same wherever it is found.

If the many chemical reactions by which a bread mold builds its

This experiment demonstrates how a defective gene is isolated and identified in *Neurospora*. By previous culture analysis, sex A has been found incapable of growing in a medium that lacks vitamins. This means that it is defective in a gene that synthesizes a vitamin; now the question is, which vitamin? The answer is obtained by planting spores from the strain in minimal media, each of which is supplemented by a single vitamin. The mold will then grow in the culture containing the vitamin which it has lost the power to produce; in this case, pantothenic acid. With this fact determined, a continuation of the experiment shows that the deficiency involves a single gene. A wild strain of the mold, called sex a and possessing normal genetic structure, is crossed with sex A, now known to be defective in the pantothenic acid gene. All the spores from this union flourish in a medium containing pantothenic acid, but when they are planted in a medium not supplemented with this vitamin, only four of the cultures grow. This proves that one gene is involved.

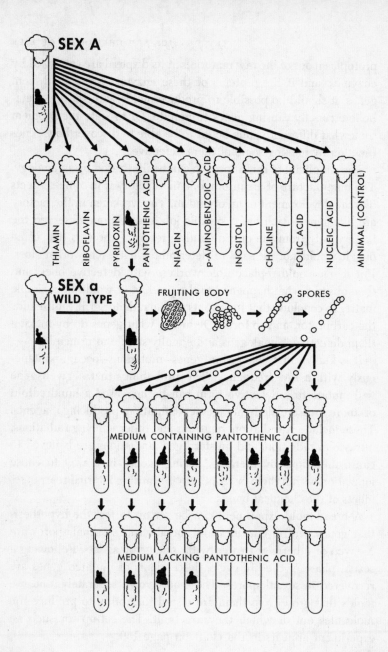

SEX A

THIAMIN
RIBOFLAVIN
PYRIDOXIN
PANTOTHENIC ACID
NIACIN
p-AMINOBENZOIC ACID
INOSITOL
CHOLINE
FOLIC ACID
NUCLEIC ACID
MINIMAL (CONTROL)

SEX a
WILD TYPE

FRUITING BODY   SPORES

MEDIUM CONTAINING PANTOTHENIC ACID

MEDIUM LACKING PANTOTHENIC ACID

159

protoplasm out of the raw materials at its disposal are catalyzed by enzymes, and if the proteins of these enzymes are copied from genes, it should be possible to produce molds with specific metabolic errors by causing genes to mutate. Or to state the problem somewhat differently, one ought to be able to discover how genes function by making some of them defective.

The simplicity of this approach can be illustrated by an analogy. The manufacture of an automobile in a factory is in some respects like the development of an organism. The workmen in the factory are like genes—each has a specific job to do. If one observed the factory only from the outside and in terms of the cars that come out, it would not be easy to determine what each worker does. But if one could replace able workers with defective ones, and then observe what happened to the product, it would be a simple matter to conclude that Jones puts on the radiator grill, Smith adds the carburetor, and so forth. Deducing what genes do by making them defective is analogous and equally simple in principle.

It is known that changes in genes—mutations—occur spontaneously with a low frequency. The probability that a given gene will mutate to a defective form can be increased a hundredfold or more by so-called mutagenic (mutation producing) agents. These include X-radiation, neutrons and other ionizing radiations, ultraviolet radiation, and mustard gas. Radiations are believed to cause mutations by literally "hitting" genes in a way to cause ionization within them or by otherwise causing internal rearrangements of the chemical bonds.

A bread-mold experiment can be set up to test the hypothesis that genes control enzymes and metabolism. Asexual spores are X-rayed or otherwise treated with mutagenic agents. Following a sexual phase of the life cycle, descendants of mutated genes are recovered in sexual spores. These are grown separately, and the molds that grow from them are tested for ability to produce the molecules out of which they are built. The set-up for such an experiment appears in the chart on page 159.

Following heavy ultraviolet treatment, about two sexual spores out of every hundred tested carry defective forms of those genes which are necessary for the production of essential substances. For example, a particular strain of *Neurospora* cannot manufacture the B-vitamin pantothenic acid. For normal growth it requires an external supply of this vitamin just as human beings do.

How do we know that the inability of the mold to produce its own pantothenic acid involves a gene defect? The only way this question can be answered at present is by seeing if inability to make pantothenic acid behaves in crosses as a single unit of inheritance.

The answer is that it does. If the mold that cannot make pantothenic acid is crossed with a normal strain of the other sex, the resulting spore sacs invariably contain four spores that produce molds like one parent and four that produce strains like the other parent. Four daughter molds out of each set of eight from a spore sac are able to make pantothenic acid, and four are not.

In a similar way, genes concerned with many other specific bread-mold chemical reactions have been mutated. In each case that has been studied in sufficient detail to be sure of the relation, it has been found that single genes are directly concerned with single chemical reactions.

Bread-mold studies have contributed strong support to the hypothesis that each gene controls a single protein. But they have not proved it to the satisfaction of all biologists. There remains a possibility that some genes possess several distinct functions and that such genes were automatically excluded by the experimental procedure followed.

The general question of how proteins are synthesized by living organisms is one of the great unsolved problems of biology. Until we have made headway toward its solution, it will not be possible to understand growth, normal or abnormal, in anything but superficial terms.

Do all organisms have genes? All sexually reproducing organisms that have been investigated by geneticists demonstrably possess them. Until recently there was no simple way of determining whether bacteria and viruses also have them. As a result of very recent investigations it has been found that some bacteria and some bacterial viruses perform a kind of sexual reproduction in which hereditary units like genes can be quite clearly shown.

By treatment of bacteria with mutagenic agents, mutant types can be produced that parallel in a striking manner those found in the bread mold. This parallelism makes it almost certain that bacterial genes are functionally like the genes of molds.

So we can sum up by asserting that genes are irreducible units of inheritance in viruses, single-celled organisms and in many-celled plants and animals. They are probably nucleoproteins that serve as patterns from which new genes are copied and from which nongenic proteins and other large molecules are produced with configurations that correspond to those of the gene templates.

It is likely that life first arose on earth as a genelike unit capable of multiplication and mutation. Through natural selection of the fittest of these units and combinations of them, more complex forms of life gradually evolved.

ENZYMES
by John Pfeiffer

SOME THREE MILLION of your red blood cells die every second. Or, to look at it another way, three million red cells are born every second, because the body continuously calls up reserves to keep the total count the same. The entire red-cell population is replaced in about three months, and cycles of birth and death turn even faster among the molecules in the plasma of the blood. This rapid molecular turnover goes on in relatively solid tissues as well as in the circulating blood. Deposits of fat, which were once believed to serve as warehouses for the storage of food reserves, are more like department stores during the Christmas rush. They seethe with biochemical activity, decomposition and synthesis neatly balancing each other so that within a few months entirely new fat deposits are created. The same goes for connective tissue, tendons and ligaments, blood-vessel walls, muscles. Swift changes occur even in the bones as the links of molecular chains are split and welded again in the ceaseless round of metabolism.

Yet the cycles of breakdown and synthesis proceed in the face of an apparent paradox. The great majority of biochemical reactions do not take place spontaneously. When they are tried in laboratory glassware, most chemical constituents of life combine or decompose at a rate far too slow for the pace of metabolism. The average protein must be boiled for 24 hours in a solution of 20 per cent hydrochloric acid to be thoroughly broken down. The body does the same thing in four hours or less, and without high temperatures and strong acids.

The phenomenon that makes life possible is catalysis—the action of certain substances that speed up chemical reactions thousands

163

of times without themselves being changed. Industrial chemistry uses catalysts in the cracking of petroleum, in the synthesis of ammonia, and in many other processes; organisms use them to help build tissues and to degrade foodstuffs to simpler materials, as in the case of the four-hour breakdown of proteins. The catalysts of life are called biocatalysts, or enzymes, and the rise of biology has come with an increased understanding of what they are, what they accomplish, and how they work.

Enzymes are unaffected by the reactions they produce; they are destroyed only by wear and tear or poisoning. They operate in amazingly small concentrations. A single cell has been estimated to contain about 100,000 enzyme molecules to accelerate its 1,000 to 2,000 chemical reactions—an average of only about 50 to 100 molecules for each process. A single molecule of the enzyme that splits hydrogen peroxide into water and oxygen (and creates the white foam when the antiseptic is placed on a wound), can transform more than 5 million peroxide molecules a minute. Other enzymes transform from 1,000 to more than 500,000 molecules in the same time.

Investigation has shown that these biochemical middlemen play a significant role in every vital process. They are key substances in the photosynthetic reactions that build plant tissues from water, carbon dioxide and sunlight. Enzymes turn leaves red and yellow in the fall, make the freshly cut surface of an apple or potato brown, convert grape juice into wine, and grain mash into whisky. But the chemical processes in which they participate are so obscure that it has taken centuries to elucidate a few fundamental principles, and every month new facts are published which promise to alter many currently accepted ideas.

The first enzyme was obtained in pure form and identified chemically by James B. Sumner of Cornell University in 1926. For nine years Sumner had been working to isolate an enzyme from the jack bean. The enzyme was urease, which decomposes the metabolic waste product, urea. Urease, like many other enzymes, is named after the substance on which it acts. The problem was to find a solvent that would dissolve urease and not other chemicals, and a substance that would then precipitate the enzyme.

The final process was, in Sumner's words, "absurdly simple." One day in April of 1926 he mixed jack-bean meal with acetone, a solvent that had been suggested by his former biochemistry professor at Harvard, and allowed the solution to filter overnight. Next morning he examined a drop of the filtrate under the microscope and saw something he had not seen before—tiny octahedral crystals. Then he centrifuged the crystals out of solution, concentrated them and found that the new solution possessed very strong urease activity. That afternoon Sumner telephoned his wife the news that was to win him a Nobel prize twenty-one years later: "I have crystallized the first enzyme." Urease turned out to be a protein with a molecular weight of 483,000. (One unit of molecular weight equals the weight of one hydrogen atom.)

Once the correct procedure had been found, it was easy to isolate urease. But there is no single process for the crystallization of all enzymes. To purify pepsin John H. Northrop of the Rockefeller Institute for Medical Research in Princeton, who with Wendell M. Stanley of the same institution shared the 1947 Nobel prize with Sumner, needed a far more complex process. He announced the method in 1930, nearly a century after pepsin had first been identified in the digestive juices. One of Northrop's chief problems was to precipitate pepsin without destroying it. It is a protein (as are all of the 40-odd enzymes isolated to date) and the molecular structure of protein is both exceedingly complex and maintained by a balance of electrical forces so delicate that a slight change in the chemical environment may distort it into a tangled mass which cannot be restored to the original pattern. That is what happens, for instance, when an egg is boiled and the white coagulates. To overcome this "denaturing," Northrop developed a precipitation technique that has since been used to crystallize several other enzymes.

165

The fermentation of sugar, yielding alcohol, is an admirable illustration of the detailed chemical processes engineered by enzymes. In the early days of enzyme study it was thought that this was accomplished by the single catalyst, zymase, and the glucose-to-alcohol reaction was represented by the following uncomplicated formula:

$$\text{C}_6\text{H}_{12}\text{O}_6 \xrightarrow{\text{zymase}} 2\,\text{CO}_2 + 2\,\text{CH}_3\text{CH}_2\text{OH}$$

This is a chemical statement to the effect that one molecule of glucose, catalyzed by zymase, yields two molecules of carbon dioxide and two of ethyl alcohol. But if fermentation were such a single-step process, it has been calculated, most of the resulting energy would appear as useless heat. Actually fermentation directly involves at least 12 enzymes—and it took hundreds of research workers from more than a dozen countries to unravel nature's scheme for altering glucose.

The molecule of glucose is built around a chain of six carbon atoms, the splitting of which is a crucial step in the fermentation process. Before this step can be taken, however, glucose must be suitably prepared for its destruction. Three enzymes transform glucose for the splitting, and nine more are involved in the remaining steps which lead to ethyl alcohol. This outline of the process is a poor reflection of the detailed chemical processes that propel it.

The splitting of the carbon chain of glucose involves one of the most significant of all biochemical cycles. It requires a large amount of chemical energy, and the source is adenosine triphosphate, or ATP. The energy is obtained from one of ATP's potent phosphate groups, indicated by the two right-hand P's in the following simplified formula:

$$\text{Adenosine}-(\text{P})\sim(\text{P})\sim(\text{P})$$

The two right-hand phosphate groups are attached by chemical bonds which yield 12,000 calories of energy when they break. (The left-hand group yields only 2,000 calories.) The bonds may be considered a sort of "cement" of electrons holding the phosphate groups. Oscillating back and forth at high speed, the electrons endow the phosphate groups with an extra reactivity. The specific usefulness of ATP is that enzymes can transfer its phosphate groups to other substances—along with the energy of their oscillating bonds.

The energy that drives the cycles of fermentation is first obtained by splitting off the right-hand phosphate group and attaching it to glucose; this step, catalyzed by the enzyme hexokinase, leaves adenosine diphosphate (ADP) and a glucose phosphate which is catalyzed to a fructose monophosphate. Transforming this latter substance to fructose diphosphate means splitting another section from another ATP molecule.

At this stage the process leaves two ADP molecules wandering about with missing groups. Unless they are rebuilt as ATP, the entire cycle will grind to a stop. The deficit is made up during the next steps of fermentation when the six-carbon chain is finally split and two inorganic (non-ATP) phosphates are taken up into an intermediate compound. These inorganic phosphates, however, are low in energy content, and ATP will only accept the high-energy variety. The cell therefore uses an enzyme called triosephosphate dehydrogenase to remove two hydrogen atoms, which transform low-energy phosphates into high-energy phosphates.

The potent phosphate groups are then split off by another enzyme and attached to the two dismembered ADP molecules, forming ATP. The energy supply is thus sustained—but the cell does better than that. During the next stages two extra high-energy phosphate groups are created and passed back to other ADP molecules. This bonus may be used to accelerate fermentation or to provide the energy needed for the growth and reproduction of yeast cells.

There is still one biochemical loose end. During the manufac-

167

ture of high-energy phosphate bonds, two hydrogen atoms have been lost. These are picked up by a special hydrogen carrier called coenzyme I. This substance now cannot participate in later reactions and, again, the entire cycle would break down unless it included a mechanism for freeing coenzyme I of its hydrogen. The opportunity comes at the very last step of fermentation, after pyruvic acid has been converted to acetaldehyde and carbon dioxide. Carbon dioxide goes off as a gas. Acetaldehyde, which remains, is just two hydrogen atoms short of being ethyl alcohol, the final product of the fermentation. The missing atoms are naturally presented by the hydrogen-bearing coenzyme I, and the latter is restored to perform its function.

This completes the fermentation process and some of its interrelated systems. Ethyl alcohol can then be taken internally and used to interfere with human enzyme systems. Incidentally, for every 99 parts of ethyl alcohol, yeast produces one part of fusel oil, a mixture of various higher alcohols which is not only responsible for most of the flavor of liquor but also for hangovers.

While some biologists traced the intricate cycles of fermentation, others studied the mechanism of muscle. Gradually, first from fragments of evidence and finally from an imposing structure of knowledge, both groups began to realize that the workings of yeast and muscle cells were very much alike. In fact, the processes that change malt and hops to beer, and those that provide the energy for an Olympic sprinter have 14 steps—and 11 of the 14 are exactly the same for the two types of process. The workings of the great ATP cycle and the wheel-within-a-wheel coenzyme I cycle are the same in both cases. One important difference is that in muscle contraction pyruvic acid is broken down to lactic acid instead of ethyl alcohol. The lactic acid is then carried by the bloodstream to the liver, where the reverse of the 14-step process builds it into animal starch, or glycogen. (Muscles cannot utilize glucose.) Another important difference is that the breakdown of glycogen yields three instead of two "bonus" ATP molecules. Muscles attain an efficiency of 60 per cent or better, as compared with the 50 per cent efficiency reached in modern steam turbines.

ATP not only supplies energy in muscle contraction, but also plays an important role in the workings of the nervous system. Nerve cells build up one of their essential chemicals, acetylcholine, with the aid of the enzyme choline acetylase, and the synthesis requires energy from ATP. That it may also be associated with the enzyme systems necessary for the movement of single-celled organisms is indicated in at least one case, the wriggling of sperm toward the unfertilized egg.

Water is the medium for the majority of biochemical processes. In water the molecules of life are in ceaseless thermal motion, occasionally reacting when they collide with one another. Essentially the function of an enzyme is to increase the rate of reaction. In a solution without enzymes the chance that a molecular collision will result in a reaction may be a trillion to one. If the appropriate enzyme is present, the probability will be much increased. To use the gambling term, enzymes lower the odds. The question is how they perform this mathematical feat by chemical means.

Any explanation of the phenomenon must account for certain experimental facts. One of the most obvious is that a given enzyme does not speed reactions among all the molecules of protoplasm. If this were the case, the result would be biochemical chaos. Actually enzymes are highly specific, producing reactive collisions only among the molecules of selected compounds. These compounds are generally known as substrates.

A spectacular example of enzyme specificity involves molecules that are made up of exactly the same atoms in different structural arrangements. Such close chemical relatives are known as isomers. In 1860 Pasteur discovered that tartaric acid, a by-product of wine fermentation, exists in two forms. When a beam of polarized light was transmitted through crystals of tartaric acid, some crystals turned the plane of polarization to the right, while others turned it to the left by exactly the same amount. Since both types of tartaric acid are identical in chemical composition, the difference must be in the arrangement of their atoms.

It has been shown that such pairs of crystals—called dextrorotary and levorotary—are found among many compounds, and are related to one another as an object to its mirror image or as a right-hand to a left-hand glove. Enzymes can make the subtle distinction between isomers. The muscle enzyme lactic dehydrogenase, for example, acts on levorotary lactic acid but has absolutely no effect on its mirror image, dextrorotary lactic acid.

Some enzymes are even more selective. The so-called hydrolytic enzymes, as an example, are involved in the following general type of reaction:

$$A - B + H_2O \longrightarrow AOH + BH$$

Here A — B represents a molecule consisting of two parts connected by a chemical linkage. Some enzymes will break down any molecule with a particular linkage regardless of the nature of the linked structures; others demand not only the right linkage but also the right part, say the B structure. Still other enzymes, the most specific of all, operate only on molecules that satisfy the three-way requirement that both the A and B parts and their linkage must be of a particular kind.

A more detailed explanation of what specificity means is furnished by the phenomenon of competitive inhibition. The enzyme succinic dehydrogenase catalyzes the breakdown of succinic acid and nothing else. Its effectiveness is considerably reduced, however, if malonic acid, the structure of which closely resembles that of succinic acid, is added to the solution. Experiments show that malonic acid, while not being changed itself, apparently attaches itself to the enzyme and takes it out of circulation by occupying a position on its molecule that would normally be filled by succinic acid. In other words, malonic acid seems to compete with succinic for an active region of the enzyme molecule.

These and other experiments suggest an attractive analogy to explain specificity. It is a theory which some protein chemists label "philosophy," although they concede that philosophy can be useful. The enzyme molecule can be visualized as a "lock" with notches and indentations of a particular pattern; the substrate molecule, in this case succinic acid, is the "key," and its configura-

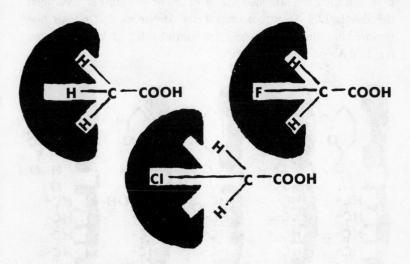

Lock and key theory explains why enzymes are specific to certain compounds and how their action can be inhibited by similar compounds. Here at left acetic acid fits an enzyme (black) and the reaction works. When a fluorine atom is substituted for a hydrogen atom, forming monofluoroacetate, the fit is close enough to occupy the enzyme and to block its reaction with acetic acid. However, when a chlorine atom replaces the fluorine atom (monochloroacetate), the key fits so poorly that the enzyme does not accept it. The compound therefore does not rob acetic acid of its enzyme.

tions mesh into the enzyme pattern. Malonic acid, a very similar key, will fit the lock, but not perfectly. The fit is good enough to keep out succinic acid, but not good enough to unlock the door—hence the door stays closed. Perhaps the most brilliant experimental evidence for such a concept, adduced by E. S. G. Barron and his associates at the University of Chicago, involves three closely similar substances: acetic acid, monofluoroacetate and monochloroacetate. The only difference among them is that one hydrogen of acetic acid is replaced by a fluorine atom in monofluoroacetate, and by a chlorine atom in monochloroacetate. The links between each of the three atoms and the rest of the molecule to which they are attached are of different length. For hydrogen the link is 1.09 Angstrom units (one Angstrom unit equals one hundred millionth centimeter); for fluorine it is 1.41 A.; for chlorine it is 1.76 A.

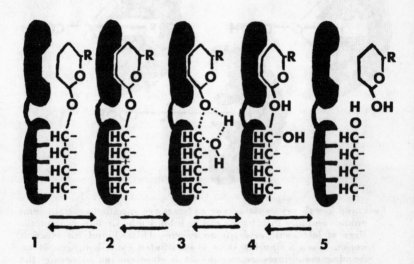

How enzymes may work is illustrated by this theoretical example. The enzyme, drawn in black, has two active parts which fit the molecule on which they act (1). When the enzyme combines with the molecule (2), its active parts deform the molecule in such a way (3, 4) that it is broken down (5) into two molecules, in this case sugar and alcohol.

An enzyme catalyzes the oxidation of acetic acid (a process involved in fat metabolism) and presumably its molecule contains "notches" into which the acid fits. The addition of monofluoroacetate to the solution completely inhibits the oxidation, meaning that this compound also fits the enzyme molecule. Monochloro-acetate, however, appears not to fit, for it has no effect on the enzyme's ability to oxidize acetic acid. In other words, the tiny difference in length between the link of the fluorine-containing inhibitor and that of the ineffective chlorine compound (.35 A., or about 1/762,000,000 inch) is enough to prevent a sufficiently close lock-key fit.

The lock-key theory implies that there is some sort of fleeting union between enzyme and substrate, an implication which has been backed by many experiments. As a matter of fact, the spectroscope has permitted biologists to "see" the union taking place. This was attempted for the first time twelve years ago by Kurt G. Stern, then at Yale University. Using the enzyme catalase and a hydrogen peroxide derivative as substrate, he observed first the spectral light pattern characteristic of catalase and then a new pattern, presumably that of the enzyme-substrate union. A short while afterward, however, the original catalase spectrum appeared again, indicating that the enzyme had performed its duty and was ready for more work.

What is the purpose of the brief combination of an enzyme with its substrate? The answer to the question hinges on a fact mentioned earlier: that not all collisions between molecules produce chemical reactions. In a 100-cubic-centimeter solution of ethyl bromide and diethyl sulfide, for instance, there are 1.6×10^{34} (16 million billion billion billion) collisions a second, but fewer than one out of every billion billion collisions results in a chemical reaction. The reason for this low proportion of successful hits is that molecules are relatively stable structures, and most of them bounce off each other a bit jarred but essentially unscathed.

Now enzymes do not increase the speed of molecules in solution, nor do they increase the frequency of collisions. Instead they increase the number of fruitful collisions by weakening the structure of substrate molecules so that they react more readily. In

173

combining briefly with its substrate (in the case of catalase the combination lasts less than one 85,000th of a second), an enzyme somehow distorts the architecture of the substrate molecule, converting it from a relatively stable to a highly reactive state. There is evidence that in some cases this effect is achieved by removing electrons and transforming the substrate molecule into a charged ion.

Chemical changes, however, do not necessarily take place simply because a substrate molecule has fitted itself into its enzyme mold and has been activated. With certain enzymes like pepsin, to be sure, this two-molecule union seems to be sufficient for completion of the substrate-converting process. But more often than not a third substance that is not a protein is an added requirement. Catalase, peroxidase and other enzymes seem to have such accessory substances more or less permanently attached to their proteins. These substances are therefore called "prosthetic groups." Many enzymes, however, apparently require only that the accessory substances be available in solution as so-called coenzymes. This field of inquiry is one of the most active and controversial in enzyme research, and the entire question of enzyme auxiliaries needs considerable clarifying. This much is known: in most enzyme processes the protein alone is not enough to speed chemical reactions. Unless coenzyme I is present in the alcohol fermentation system previously described, the process breaks down.

Even more obscure than the mechanism of enzyme action are the factors that control enzyme reactions. What is it that determines when and how quickly enzyme activities shall take place in nerve cells, muscle cells and all of the other specialized units that make up the higher plant and animal organisms?

There is reason to believe that hormones play an important part in controlling and coordinating the workings of enzyme systems. The most significant finding along these lines was made about two years ago by W. H. Price, Carl Cori and S. P. Colowick at Washington University in St. Louis. They discovered that hormones play an essential part in the enzyme system that maintains the balance between sugar in the blood and glycogen in the liver. There is a delicate equilibrium between the hormone insulin, which tends to lower the amount of sugar in the blood by promoting the storage of glycogen in the liver, and a presumed diabetogenic hormone secreted by the pituitary gland, which promotes the metabolism of glycogen and hence tends to raise the concentration of sugar. Diabetes may be the result either of too little insulin or too much of the pituitary hormone. The Washington University group suggested that this upset in hormone balance was directly connected with hexokinase, the same enzyme that initiates alcoholic fermentation.

Hexokinase is utilized in the liver to add a phosphate group to glucose, a preliminary step essential to the storage of sugar. The pituitary hormone, however, inhibits hexokinase activity. Whether it is overproduced or insulin is underproduced, the effect is the same: a relative excess of the diabetogenic hormone, subnormal storage of glycogen in the liver, and rising sugar levels in the blood. The discovery of this process is one of the first connections established between hormones and enzymes. Other hormones, including those that produce dwarfs and giants, probably influence growth and metabolism in a similar manner.

Such speculation brings us again to the notion of enzymes that can be inhibited and activated. Does the diabetogenic hormone inhibit hexokinase by providing substances that occupy strategic parts of the enzyme molecule and thus prevent it from working on its normal substrate? And does insulin counteract the inhibiting effect by removing these substances and "unmasking" the enzyme? Only further investigation can answer these questions, but it is known that the unmasking effect plays a significant role in the control of enzyme action during many biological processes. For example, pepsin, the function of which is to digest proteins, does not enter the stomach ready to act; it is secreted by the stomach walls as the inert substance pepsinogen, which is promptly converted to pepsin by the hydrochloric acid of the gastric juices. The conversion is accompanied by a drop in molecular weight from 42,000 to 38,000, and this may be interpreted as the removal of a protein fragment that masks pepsin action.

An example of mass unmasking is familiar to embryologists. An unfertilized egg cell is fully prepared for the most spectacular burst of biological energy known. It contains structural materials, ATP as a source of energy, and hundreds of enzymes that will engineer the building of a tree or a man from a tiny blob of protoplasm. The enzymes, however, are blocked, probably by specialized coatings, until fertilization takes place. Then, by an unidentified mechanism, the blocking substances are dissolved, hundreds of reactions are set off at once, and the cell begins to grow and divide.

The patient investigation of enzyme action and enzyme control has brought added insight to a whole constellation of biological and medical problems. Enzymes not only speed the vital processes of the developing egg, but play a fascinating part in the act of fertilization. An unfertilized egg is protected by a tough coating of cells cemented with a substance called hyaluronic acid. The sperm carries the enzyme hyaluronidase specifically to break up the barrier and penetrate within.

There is evidence that the single sperm which accomplishes fertilization does not contain enough of the enzyme to break down the barrier by itself, and that the unsuccessful sperm cells must contribute their hyaluronidase. This explanation accounts for the fact that perhaps millions of sperm are necessary for fertilization, although only one penetrates the egg. Working on the theory that some cases of human sterility may be due to a lack of hyaluronidase, some physicians have recently administered extra amounts to a few selected patients and, according to preliminary announcements, normal pregnancy has resulted. Whether or not this simple treatment proves effective in a significant number of cases, any successful treatment for sterility will require an intimate understanding of the enzymes concerned.

176

Enzymes have also been identified with the toxins of infectious diseases. Thus *Clostridium welchii*, the rod-shaped organism most commonly found in gas gangrene, releases an enzyme called lecithinase. This destroys red blood cells by disintegrating the substance lecithin in their walls. (The same lecithinase is one of the poisons in cobra and rattlesnake venom.) The germ also liberates an enzyme that dissolves the protein connective tissue of muscle, and the "gas" of gas gangrene is produced by a group of enzymes that accelerate a pathological form of fermentation. The effects of many drugs and poisons are similarly tied up with enzyme reactions.

The chemical study of certain coenzymes has had unexpected medical consequences. In 1932 it was found that an essential part of the coenzyme I molecule was nicotinic acid, and three years later C. A. Elvehjem and his associates at the University of Wisconsin identified the substance as the anti-pellagra vitamin. Other vitamins definitely known to be part of coenzyme molecules include B-1, B-2 and B-6. Whether all vitamins are parts of coenzymes remains to be seen, but the possibility is particularly strong for those factors of nutrition that are needed in "trace" quantities. In amounts of less than one ten-millionth of an ounce the new B-12 factor is sufficient to produce measurable rises in the blood counts of anemia patients.

Vitamins are as necessary to some harmful bacteria as they are to human life. This fact has opened the way for putting the competitive inhibition of enzymes to medical use. The possibility was discovered by accident after the introduction of sulfa drugs, though for a long while their effectiveness in curbing germs was a mystery. Then it was observed that the ability of the drugs to inhibit the growth of bacteria was considerably reduced in the presence of para-aminobenzoic acid (PAB), a member of the vitamin B complex and an essential factor in the growth of many organisms. A comparison of the molecular structures of sulfanilamide and the acid soon indicated the reason for the phenomenon.

Germs that need the vitamin presumably incorporate it into their

177

metabolic processes as part of a coenzyme, and things go beautifully until sulfanilamide comes upon the biochemical scene. This sulfa drug is a very close chemical relative of PAB, which is the secret of its medical effectiveness. The resemblance is so close that the bacterium cannot tell the difference and takes up sulfanilamide as if it were a real food factor. By the time the mistake is discovered, the false "vitamin" has been drawn into the enzyme system and jammed the works.

The part played by vitamins and other accessories in enzyme action also throws new light on the importance of trace elements in plant and animal life. In 1895 thousands of sheep on Australian ranches were dying of "bush sickness." Since the disease closely resembled anemia, ranchers tried feeding the animals large doses of iron. The treatment worked in some cases and not in others, the difference depending on the source of the iron.

So the Australian government imported iron ores from all over the world and compared the samples. After a series of elaborate analyses, it was found that the iron which helped to cure bush sickness contained tiny amounts of cobalt. A sheep's daily requirements were calculated, and it was found that about a millionth of an ounce of cobalt was enough to prevent the malady.

The need for such elements may be connected with the efficient working of enzyme systems, for many enzymes are known to contain or to require the presence of metallic elements in small amounts. One of the key steps in alcoholic fermentation involves an enzyme called enolase, which requires the presence of magnesium ions before it can take effect. Hexokinase, similarly, cannot work without magnesium.

Enzymes have still other practical applications. By breeding improved strains of microorganisms and investigating their enzymes, research workers have increased the efficiency of alcoholic fermentation in the beer, wine and liquor industries.

Enzymes are also used to obtain heating gas, fertilizer and many other valuable materials from sewage and industrial waste. They

178

tenderize meat, tan leather, turn cornstarch into syrups and sugars, and help in the making of dozens of products in the cosmetic, textile and baking industries.

From the lofty perspective of science the fundamental problem is not industrial utility or even the artful crystallization of pure enzymes. The most challenging question is how the human body, or any organism, manufactures enzymes. An enzyme is a protein built up by the body from amino acids and peptide chains. If we assume that an enzyme may be synthesized as simply as possible, it is created when two protein fragments are pieced together by a single enzyme. If that is the process, how is the ultimate enzyme itself synthesized?

The only way of surmounting the difficulty is to assume that certain molecules are capable of forming exact replicas of themselves. This is to say that they act as enzymes for their own synthesis. This is reproduction at the molecular level. Genes, the units of heredity, have been assumed to be such substances. Viruses likewise are autocatalytic. There is some speculation that genes are the ultimate enzyme-makers.

The red bread mold *Neurospora* is an experimental organism used in the study of this problem. In a whole series of experiments in which mutated *Neurospora* strains were created by ultraviolet radiation that knocked out a single gene in each case, each missing gene resulted in the organism's inability to synthesize a specific foodstuff, indicating that the heredity-transmitting molecules are directly connected with the production of enzymes. In fact, it has recently been indicated that a strain of *Neurospora* lacking a particular gene actually lacks an enzyme which can be extracted from strains having a full complement of genes.

To proceed from *Neurospora* to man, there are certain human diseases that are due to the deficiency of single enzymes. Significantly, these diseases also are inherited according to strict Mendelian laws. The lack of a single enzyme in the metabolism of the amino-acid phenylalanine is sufficient to cause a form of mental defectiveness, while another missing link in the same system is responsible for albinism. Since each of these diseases can ultimately be traced to the hereditary defect of a single gene, and the agency in each case is a missing enzyme, circumstantial evidence argues strongly for the theory that each gene is associated with the making of a single enzyme.

So enzymes bring us finally to the very core of the cell, and to the core of all biological problems. The solution of these problems depends more and more on our understanding of proteins, and particularly of enzymes, self-duplicating and otherwise.

THE METABOLISM OF FATS

by David E. Green

Aɴɪᴍᴀʟs ɢᴇɴᴇʀᴀᴛᴇ nearly all their energy by oxidizing sugars and fats. Biochemists have known for some time how the body oxidizes sugars, but only within the past year have they filled in an equally detailed picture of how it oxidizes fats. It had taken some fifty years of intensive work in laboratories all over the world to complete the picture. The Nobel prize committee recognized the importance of phases of that work when it awarded the 1953 prize in physiology and medicine to two men who had made key discoveries. The history of the research on oxidation of fatty acids is one of the truly adventurous episodes in biochemistry.

The substances called fats consist of a combination of a fatty acid with an alcohol, such as glycerol. The part of this combination that the body burns for fuel is the fatty acid. It is a hydrocarbon—the kind of stuff man has been burning for fuel ever since he lit the first wax candle. A fatty acid is a hydrocarbon with a carboxyl group ($COOH$) attached at one end of the molecule. In the common fatty acids the hydrocarbon chain is usually 16 to 20 carbon atoms long.

The process nature has developed for burning fatty acids in the body is roundabout, complex and under beautiful control. The only way a chemist can reconstruct it is from deductions based on examination of the combustion products, and the main problem has been to catch these products at the successive stages of the combustion.

In 1904 the German biochemist Franz Knoop opened the door to an understanding of fatty acid oxidation with a brilliantly thought-out experiment. He conceived the idea of attaching a fatty acid to a more obdurate substance, as one would fasten a piece of cheese

181

to a wooden block, and then examining the products when the animal body so to speak "chopped off" (oxidized) successive slices of the "cheese." The block he used was the benzene ring. Attachment of a fatty acid to this ring forms what organic chemists call a phenyl fatty acid. Knoop synthesized two kinds of phenyl fatty acids—one with an even number of carbon atoms in the hydrocarbon chain, the other with an odd number. Then he fed them to experimental animals for oxidation and analyzed the animals' urine to find out how they had "degraded" (chopped down) the fatty acids.

As he had hoped, the odd-numbered and even-numbered phenyl fatty acids yielded different end products. The even-numbered chain was reduced to one carbon atom plus the carboxyl group, i.e., two carbon atoms in all. This is phenyl acetic acid. The odd-numbered chain was degraded to just the carboxyl group, attached directly to the benzene ring, that is, benzoic acid. From these results Knoop, and independently the chemist Henry Dakin, concluded that fatty acids were chopped down two carbon atoms at a time. Each chop (oxidation) removed two carbon atoms, including the one in the carboxyl group, and then a new carboxyl group was formed at the cut end of the chain. Chemists called the carbon atom that was cut from the chain the alpha atom and the one from which it was separated the beta atom, and the process became known as beta oxidation. Knoop and Dakin visualized each oxidation as taking place in four steps.

Knoop's theory hit the mark almost exactly, but it took half a century to prove the theory correct and to identify the intermediate products formed in the four steps of beta oxidation. The difficulty was that only the final product appeared in the urine, and the intermediate stages could not be isolated. The number of investigators who beat their heads against this difficulty is legion. But occasionally an ingenious experimenter had a flash of inspiration, and one inspiration led to another.

In 1906 the German chemist Gustave Embden made the first break in the wall by studying fatty acid metabolism in a single

182

organ instead of the whole animal. He separated the liver from an animal and kept it functioning by pumping nutrients into it through a closed circulation system. When he introduced fatty acids into the entering veins, he found that the isolated liver did indeed oxidize many kinds of fatty acids. But the only product he could recognize in the outgoing blood was diacetic acid—a combination of two molecules of acetic acid. This was one of the end products, not an intermediate. Yet Embden had begun to blaze the right path, though it took many years for investigators to follow it up. That path was to simplify the experimental conditions. In 1935 the English biochemist J. H. Quastel went a step further by examining fatty acid oxidation in thin slices of tissue, rather than in a whole organ. Although he obtained valuable information on the extent of combustion of fatty acids by various tissues, he too failed to isolate any intermediate products.

Then in 1939 Luis Leloir and J. M. Muñoz of Argentina reported an epoch-making discovery. They crushed liver cells and found that tiny granules from the cell, after being separated from the debris, were able to carry out fatty acid oxidation as effectively as the intact cell. No outsider can really appreciate what this meant to investigators: at last they were freed from the shackles of working with complex biological systems and could probe fatty acid oxidation at the molecular level.

At first the results were disappointing, because the oxidation products of the granules were essentially identical with those obtained in the more complex systems. But studies of the granules eventually opened a completely new approach. The cell granules, later identified as mitochondria, were found to house hundreds of enzymes which catalyzed fatty acid oxidation and other related processes. Most important, experiments with the mitochondrial system carried out in my laboratory disclosed that the fatty acids were not oxidized as such; they had to be converted to something else first. No oxidation took place unless an oxidizable substance called a "sparker" was added to the mitochondrial suspension.

However, it soon became apparent that the oxidation of the fatty acid was sparked not by the oxidation of the sparker itself but by some event which accompanied this oxidation. The tracking down of that mysterious event involved the piecing together of clues from many different investigations.

One of the clues came from the discovery of the so-called citric acid or Krebs cycle by Hans A. Krebs of England (who for his discovery was awarded half of the 1953 Nobel prize in physiology). This cycle has to do with the oxidation of pyruvic acid (a breakdown product of sugar) into carbon dioxide and water, and it takes place in five separate oxidative steps. At each step the oxidation of the intermediate product is accompanied by the simultaneous conversion of inorganic phosphate into adenosine triphosphate (ATP)—that famous substance which triggers so many chemical reactions in the cell.

Now the mysterious role of the sparker in fatty acid oxidation began to unravel. Any one of the five oxidative steps in the citric acid cycle can spark fatty acid oxidation; thus the sparker could be any of the four substances formed from pyruvic acid during the operation of the cycle. It was apparent that the oxidation of the sparker led to the formation of ATP, and ATP in turn converted the fatty acid to something else. What that something was, and how it took part in the oxidative chopping down of the fatty acid, became the next important question to be answered. And here the chief clues stemmed from the work of Fritz A. Lipmann of Harvard University (winner of the other half of the 1953 Nobel physiology prize).

In 1945 Lipmann discovered in animal tissues a substance which was essential for the utilization of acetic acid in the body. He named it coenzyme A: a coenzyme is much smaller than an enzyme (about the relative size of the moon compared to the earth), is not a protein and is usually resistant to breakdown by heat. Lipmann and his group proceeded to purify and analyze coenzyme A. It was found to be made of three main building stones: (1) pantothenic

184

acid (one of the B vitamins), (2) a phosphate related to ATP and (3) thioethanolamine (discovered by Esmond E. Snell of Wisconsin).

Lipmann recognized that the acetic acid participating in cell reactions is not the original form but a more reactive derivative. He and his colleagues found many signs pointing to the likelihood that acetic acid interacted with coenzyme A to form acetyl coenzyme A. But he was not able to isolate that product. It remained for Feodor Lynen of Munich to recognize what made coenzyme A tick. That knowledge provided him with the needed clue which enabled him to announce in 1951 success in isolating acetyl coenzyme A from yeast.

There was a striking parallel to the case of the unknown active form of the fatty acids, but it was not immediately recognized as such. The first to draw the parallel were the microbiologists Horace A. Barker and Earl Stadtman at the University of California. They had been studying a microorganism which showed the remarkable capacity to synthesize fatty acids in the absence of oxygen in a medium containing ethyl alcohol as the sole source of carbon. In effect this organism was carrying out fatty acid oxidation in reverse. Barker and Stadtman discovered that the organism needed coenzyme A for this process, and they surmised that the active form of fatty acid for which investigators had been searching was a derivative of coenzyme A, just as the active form of acetic acid was acetyl coenzyme A. In short, the x in the fatty acid equation turned out to be coenzyme A.

Biochemists were now able to get on with working out the details of fatty acid oxidation. This called for a radical change in strategy. First ways and means had to be found for preparing the various fatty acid derivatives that were oxidized. Then the enzymes which catalyzed the successive reactions had to be isolated one by one. The investigation was blocked at the outset by the scarcity of purified coenzyme A; it was available only in milligram amounts. A group of investigators at the University of Wisconsin solved this difficulty by recognizing that yeast was a rich and convenient source of the coenzyme, that the substance could readily be concentrated in charcoal chromatographic columns and that the coenzyme could then be purified by precipitation of its copper salt with a copper salt of glutathione. This made it possible to prepare coenzyme A in gram quantities instead of milligrams.

My colleagues Henry Mahler and Saleh Wakil then found a way to carry out the next step: synthesis of the needed fatty acid derivatives. They isolated from beef liver an enzyme which in the presence of ATP could convert various fatty acids into their corresponding coenzyme A derivatives. The process was uncomfortably expensive, but it could supply all the derivatives required. Then came the problem of identifying the enzyme that catalyzed each reaction. Our group at Wisconsin, following up an earlier observation by George Drysdale and Henry Lardy, who had worked only with rats, developed a technique for preparing mitochondria, in which the enzymes are housed, from slaughterhouse animals. After isolating the enzymes from the mitochondria, the Wisconsin group systematically tested them and found, as might have been expected, that there was a separate enzyme for each of the four stages in the stepwise oxidation of fatty acids. The four enzymes and the reaction products have now been identified.

Lynen in Germany, collaborating with Severo Ochoa of New York University, reached the same objectives as the Wisconsin group by a completely different stratagem. Lacking their large-scale supplies of coenzyme A and the enzyme needed to prepare coenzyme A derivatives, he hit upon the ingenious expedient of offering synthetic derivatives for the oxidation-catalyzing enzymes to act upon. He used fatty acid derivatives of thioethanolamine, which is one of the building blocks of coenzyme A and which can be synthesized in the laboratory without too much difficulty. Some of the enzymes of the fatty acid oxidizing system did act upon these synthetic derivatives, and Lynen thus was able to purify those particular enzymes. It is not often that enzymes can be fooled in this way, but Lynen's bait did the trick.

In retrospect it is now easy to see why it was so difficult to isolate the intermediate products of fatty acid oxidation. The attachment of a fatty acid to coenzyme A is like the kiss of death. Once attached, the fatty acid has no alternative but to go through the entire cycle of chemical change. Only at the end of the cycle is it possible for the end product (diacetic acid) to let go of the coenzyme. Nature has seen to it that release from the coenzyme takes place at the end of the ride and not before. This restriction makes sense from the standpoint of the cell. Since ATP has to foot the bill for making a coenzyme A derivative of the fatty acid, and since ATP is a most valuable asset which the cell can ill afford to squander, nature appears to have taken special precautions to prevent the breakdown of the coenzyme A derivatives during fatty acid oxidation.

Perhaps you are wondering how the cell gets any energy profit from the oxidation of fatty acids if ATP has to be used to initiate the process. The answer is that the chain of oxidation reactions returns as many as 100 molecules of ATP for each one invested. For each penny on deposit the cell gets back a dollar.

Why all this fuss about finding out the enzymatic details of the steps in fatty acid oxidation? Biochemists are in no position at present to say what fruits may come from it, but the study of mechanisms has in general been one of the most rewarding pursuits of biochemistry. The knowledge of the mechanism of fatty acid oxidation will permit us to probe deeply into areas which hitherto have been impenetrable. Some of the nuggets of information which it has uncovered thus far are that three B vitamins (flavin, niacin and pantothenic acid) are involved in the oxidation process, that ATP sparks it by energizing the conversion of a fatty acid to its coenzyme A derivative, that copper teams up with flavin to assist the enzyme which carries out the first oxidative step. By way of illustration of how one finding leads to another, this last discovery has led our group to the recognition that molybdenum and iron serve as functional groups in other flavin-containing enzymes not involved in fatty acid oxidation.

From the height the enzyme chemist has scaled in elucidating the oxidation of fatty acids he can see other eminences which may be approachable by similar tactics. The reverse of this oxidation process, i.e., the synthesis of long-chain fatty acids, proceeds in somewhat the same way as the synthesis of cholesterol and other steroids, of plant carotenoids (e.g., vitamin A) and of rubber. All these synthetic processes appear to depend upon the combination of the same fundamental units. They differ only in detail. In fatty acid synthesis carbon atoms join together in a linear arrangement like beads on a string. In carotenoid synthesis the only difference is that side spurs of carbon atoms are attached at regular intervals along the string. In cholesterol synthesis the string loops around and forms a series of rings. From what has been learned about the enzymes participating in fatty acid oxidation there is good reason to believe that it will be possible to carry out these synthetic processes artificially with isolated enzymes within the next five to ten years.

Our new knowledge about fatty acid oxidation may also eventually help to explain some mysteries of diabetes. Many diabetics are unable to oxidize fats completely: their urine contains abnormal amounts of products of partial oxidation. Furthermore, the amount of fat in their tissues declines to a very low level. Injections of insulin enable these patients to carry the oxidation to completion and increase remarkably their capacity to synthesize and deposit fat. It seems altogether likely that a block in the enzyme systems involved in the synthesis of fat plays a substantial part in diabetes. In this connection it should be pointed out that the same enzymes which bring about fatty acid oxidation in animal tissues can be made to work backward and under appropriate conditions synthesize fatty acids.

PART 5 CELL AND ORGANISM

I. CELL DIVISION
by Daniel Mazia

Associate professor of zoology at the University of California, Berkeley, Daniel Mazia declares that he chose that state and institution as the locale of his work because of the year-round availability of "big, ripe, juicy sea urchins," the creatures who provide his principal material for his study of cell division. He was born in Scranton, Pa., and educated at the University of Pennsylvania, where he took his doctorate under the distinguished physiologist L. V. Heilbrunn. After a year at Princeton as a National Research Fellow, he taught at the University of Missouri, remaining there until 1951, with three years out for war service as an aviation physiologist.

II. CELL DIFFERENTIATION
by C. H. Waddington

Starting his career as a geologist, C. H. Waddington became interested in evolution; that led him into genetics and that again to the mode of operation of the genes and finally into his present field of embryology and his appointment as professor of animal genetics at the University of Edinburgh. He was born in India in 1905 and was educated at Cambridge University. During the war, he was in charge of the Operational Research Section of the Coastal Command of the Royal Air Force. In 1947 he was elected a Fellow of the Royal Society. Outside of his technical field, Waddington is distinguished for his writings on the philosophy and social implications of science and is author of *The Scientific Attitude* and *Science and Ethics*.

CELL DIVISION

by Daniel Mazia

IT SEEMS to be a necessity of the biological world—though exceptions exist—that any living mass of more than microscopic size be composed of cells. The capacity of cells to grow, in the sense of adding to their content of chemical substances that do not exist in the inorganic world, is limited. In general—though again there are exceptions—a cell can only double its mass. Thus any significant growth requires the production of new cells, and this involves the process of cell division. We can add continuously to the amount of living matter only by multiplication, and the multiplication takes place by division.

All this is commonplace today, but it seemed so unreasonable a century ago that it was not even accepted by Theodor Schwann and Matthias Jakob Schleiden, the two German biologists who are generally credited with the founding of the cell theory. Cell division had actually been seen and described many times by skillful microscopists. But an observation is seldom acceptable if its consequences seem unreasonable, and the dictum that every cell must arise by the division of a pre-existing cell did seem unreasonable. Schwann and Schleiden were much more reasonable when they proposed that new cells arise by a process analogous to the formation of crystals in a solution. They were merely wrong.

We now understand the reasons why cells must always arise from cells and by a process that seems excessively complicated. It is because the history and capabilities of a cell are determined by the threadlike chromosomes in its nucleus, and the various forms of life can maintain their historical continuity only if the chromosome patterns are transmitted from cell to cell. If the biological world is essentially conservative in its tendencies, it is because the chromosomes are so stable. The elaborate process of cell division that we call mitosis perpetuates them in all their stability.

Of all the activities that we can see in the cell, mitosis is the most complicated, and its machinery is about the most elaborate that a cell can manufacture. Hereinafter we shall refer to this machinery as the mitotic apparatus. Anyone who has ever attempted to make a satisfactory diagram of the process, or teach it to a class of normally unresponsive freshmen, will grant that its complexity is real. A machine of beautiful geometric perfection is temporarily created out of the seeming formlessness of the cell and operates with exquisite co-ordination.

Let us consider what happens. We begin with the so-called "resting cell," a cell that is busy enough in other ways but has not yet gone through the travail of giving birth to two daughter cells. The chromosomes are contained in the nucleus and look like nothing at all. We know they are there from chemical and genetic data, but the lovely compact threads that we always visualize when we think of chromosomes usually are visible only during mitosis. In the resting cell there is no evidence of the mitotic apparatus, except that in favorable cases a small body appearing either single or double sometimes is detected near the surface of the nucleus. This is what we call the centriole or centrosphere.

What happens when this resting cell begins to divide may be regarded in two phases. First, the mitotic apparatus is formed. (See diagram on page 193.) The centrioles divide, separate, and as they separate throw out what seem like radiating systems of fibers, appropriately called asters. These appear to find their way to opposite poles of the cell and to be connected by fibers running from one centriole to the other. This group of fibers is called the spindle. Meanwhile the previously invisible chromosomes are becoming visible as slender threads while the nucleus fades away. Then the threads become more compact. In a most remarkable way the chromosomes find their way to the equator of the spindle; that is, a plane exactly midway between the two centrioles and at right angles to a line connecting them. Here we have the culmination of this remarkable set of preliminary maneuvers. Now the mitotic apparatus is fully formed. At some point along the way it becomes possible to observe that each of the chromosomes has doubled. More precise evidence suggests that the real duplication process has occurred much earlier than the visible appearance of twin threads. In fact, it is now thought that the duplication takes place during the resting stage, which would mean that mitosis was a process for distributing the products of a reproductive step that had already been completed.

The second and perhaps more dynamic stage of mitosis is the movement of one complete set of chromosomes to each pole, and, co-ordinated with this, the division of the whole cell so that each set of daughter chromosomes goes to one of the daughter cells. It is here that we see the mitotic apparatus in action, moving the chromosomes apart, often pushing the cell out of shape, and somehow controlling the location of the wall that will finally separate the daughter cells. Finally we have two daughter cells, each with half of the mother's substance and each with a complete set of chromosomes seemingly identical with those of the mother. These daughters go back into a resting stage by a process that roughly resembles a movie of the first steps of mitosis run backward. The chromosomes disappear from view and a nucleus is formed.

The process has many variations. In plant cells we ordinarily do not see asters. Animal cells divide by what looks like a process of pinching in two; plant cells build a new wall. In both cases the barrier between the two daughter cells is formed exactly where the equator of the spindle was located. Some single-celled animals have bizarre systems of mitosis. In the bacteria the very existence

Progress of mitosis is outlined in schematic form. As the cell prepares to divide, chromosomes appear in its nucleus. The mitotic apparatus then forms and draws the divided chromosomes apart. The cell finally pinches in two and gives rise to two new cells.

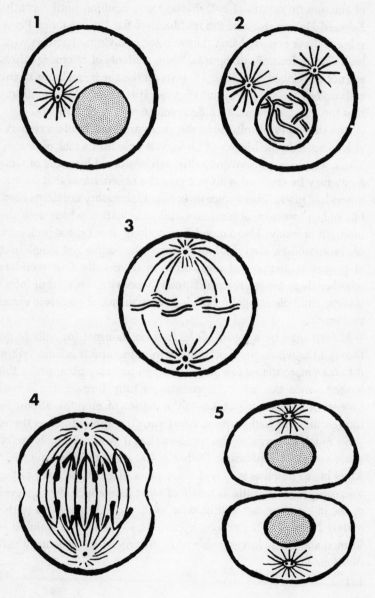

of the mitotic system of cell division was doubted until recently. Edward DeLamater and Stuart Mudd of the University of Pennsylvania have reported that they can see in dividing bacteria what look like typical mitotic figures. Some students of microorganisms are not convinced; the difficulty rests on the sheer smallness of the cells and of the alleged mitotic figures. It is nonetheless significant that the trend is toward a unified picture of how cells divide.

The discovery of mitosis in the years around 1880 is a remarkable chapter in the history of biology, if only for its lack of drama. There was no one discoverer, although Walther Flemming of Germany may be credited with unifying the observations that he and others had made. There were no brilliant laboratory accidents here, but only powers of observation and imagination which awe the biologist of today. These men knew nothing about the significance of chromosomes; they had to observe the individual stages out of proper sequence and most often in dead cells. One wonders whether there are microscopists today who with this kind of information could piece together the logical sequence of mitosis in space and time.

Mitosis may be a rapid affair. It is not unusual for cells to go through the whole process in thirty minutes, and it is unusual for it to take more than a few hours. The preparatory phases take the longest; once the mitotic apparatus is fully formed, the actual process of division may take only a matter of minutes, almost as though the cells had snapped apart once the apparatus was there.

So much happens in this process that it would scarcely make sense to ask the question: "What is the mechanism of mitosis?" Knowing as much as we do of what takes place at the level of the microscope, and as little as we do of what happens below the level of the microscope, we will be wise to restrict our questions to the material nature of the mitotic apparatus, to the way in which it is formed and to the forces involved in the crucial movements of cell division.

The symmetry of the mitotic apparatus inspired a number of interesting physical models based on the operation of electrical and magnetic forces. In most cases it would appear that the chromosomes are being pulled through a liquid by special fibers which run from the poles and are attached to a definite region of each chromosome. This region has been called by various workers the centromere, kinetochore or simply "the spindle fiber attachment." The convincing reasons for this "contractile fiber" hypothesis are two. First, each chromosome generally takes the form of the letter V or J or a rod, with the point facing the pole. This is what we would expect if a limp thread were dragged through a liquid. Second, the point of attachment is always the same for a given chromosome. If the point is eliminated when the chromosome is broken by X-rays or another agency, the chromosome does not move at all. There are, however, disturbing exceptions. Some years ago Charles W. Metz, now at the University of Pennsylvania, described a case in the fly *Sciara* in which the chromosomes pointed the wrong way! This has never been explained in terms of the contractile fiber hypothesis.

Various mechanisms have been proposed to explain the division of the cell mass, especially in those cases where a pinching or "furrow" is involved. One hypothesis involves the so-called "contractile ring." This hypothesis suggests that, at the time of division, a layer around the equator of the mitotic apparatus actually contracts and pinches the cell in two. It is based in part on some interesting experiments by Douglas Marsland of New York University. A contractile ring would have to be a rigid layer of colloid in the gel state. Such a gel, Marsland predicted, would become soft and liquid under high pressure, on the order of 500 atmospheres. Beneath the surface of cells there is a thin layer of gel called the cortex, and Marsland was able to show that the application of high pressure did make this layer more liquid. Experiments on dividing cells revealed that pressures which liquefied the cortex also prevented the cell from dividing. Whether or not the contractile ring hypothesis proves to be true, these experiments demonstrate that a semirigid cortex plays an essential part in cell division.

A more detailed hypothesis on the mechanics of cell division in cases where asters are present and a furrow is formed has been elaborated by Katsuma Dan of Tokyo Metropolitan University in Japan. Some years ago Dan devised a very simple means of following the movements of the cell surface during division. He applied tiny particles of clay to the surface of cells, and some of these adhered. Then, with great patience, he measured the distance between two particles during cell division. His results were most unexpected. At the region of the furrow, where the surface would be expected to stretch, the distance between the particles actually decreased.

As the furrow forms, the cell elongates. The spindle, too, is longer from pole to pole. Dan pictures the spindle as a stiff body that pushes the centers apart. At this point the rays of the asters, growing in all directions, appear to have joined the surface of the cell. The rays of the opposite asters cross at the equator. Dan's ingenious proposal is that, when the asters are pushed apart, the tips of the rays are brought closer together in the region where they cross. If, as he imagines, the tips are attached to the cell surface, their movement will collapse it at a point midway between the centers.

Ordinarily the asters are of equal size, and the center of the spindle is the equator of the cell; thus we expect the cell to divide into equal halves. But if one aster is much larger than the other the midpoint of the spindle will be displaced from the equator toward the smaller aster. In this case Dan predicts an unequal division, with the smaller daughter cell containing the smaller aster. This is confirmed by observation, and is a strong point in favor of his view.

In Dan's theory the work of cell division is accomplished by the push of the lengthening spindle at the time the cell is seen to divide. Last year two biologists at Cambridge University in England, M. M. Swann and J. M. Mitchison, proposed a mechanism which is a compromise between the contracting-ring theory, in which the mitotic apparatus has no role in the division of the cell mass, and Dan's theory, in which the role of the mitotic apparatus is paramount. According to Swann and Mitchison, the furrow is due to an active stretching of the cell surface by the unfolding of molecules that were previously rolled up and did not occupy as great an area. They consider that the mitotic apparatus may determine the position of the furrow and guide it inward as in Dan's model.

But neither through microscopic observation nor ingenious physical models can we achieve a feeling of intimate contact with the realities of cell division. The formulation has lacked substance, which in today's biology means a treatment in terms of identifiable molecules undergoing reactions translatable into the language of chemistry. What is the stuff of the mitotic apparatus and how are its constituents assembled into this beautiful little gadget? Answers to these questions solve no problems of mitosis, but put flesh between the bones of physical speculation and the clothing of microscopic appearance.

In the past year an opening toward the answers to these questions has been found in experiments conducted at the University of California by Dan and the author. The direct way to obtain the answers is clear enough. One should isolate the mitotic apparatus from dividing cells in pure form and in quantity and study its chemistry and its structure. Other bodies in the cell—nuclei, chromosomes, mitochondria—have been isolated and studied with great profit. But the problem here is a little more difficult. The mitotic apparatus is a temporary structure. It appears in the cell only when it is dividing, and changes continuously in the course of division. It is not freely suspended but is embedded in the substance of the cell. What is worse, it is extremely unstable in its living environment. If a dividing cell is damaged mechanically or treated with one of a number of chemicals, the mitotic apparatus simply disappears.

In order to experiment on the isolation of the mitotic apparatus in quantity, it was obviously necessary to work with a large population of cells, all of which were dividing synchronously. Dan and I were fortunate to have on hand, in the tide pools of the Pacific shore, the material of choice. For many years students of cell division have worked with the eggs of sea urchins, which may be induced to divide by fertilizing them with sperm cells. If a very large number of eggs are inseminated at a given time, all will divide synchronously. The whole mitotic process from the time of fertilization may take an hour or so, but so uniform is the cell population that 90 per cent of the cells will be seen to be forming division furrows within a period of five to ten minutes. Thus we could experiment with masses of cells which represented for the most part any desired stage of the mitotic process.

Because the mitotic apparatus is so unstable it was necessary to find a means of stopping the process with the least damage and the least chemical change. After many experiments, very cold (minus 10 degrees centigrade) dilute ethyl alcohol proved to be suitable.

Attempts to isolate the mitotic apparatus by the conventional method of mechanical disintegration of the cells were so discouraging that we turned to a fresh, though not necessarily original, approach. If the mitotic apparatus were chemically different from other things in the cell, could we not find some means of "dissolving" the cell in such a way as to liberate the apparatus?

We knew of agents that dissolve (solubilize is the more precise word) cell structures without excessive damage to the molecules of which they are composed. Foremost among them are the detergents, substances with a soaplike action. At first we worked with synthetic detergents of the varieties commonly encountered in the dishpan and the laundry tub. We found that Duponol (sodium lauryl sulfate) was effective in solubilizing the cytoplasm of the dividing sea-urchin eggs, but that it dissolved the mitotic apparatus as well.

Looking at the research in retrospect, it is evident that we should then have tested gentler detergents; it was perhaps fortunate that instead we attempted to analyze the conditions that determined whether or not a body would be solubilized by a detergent. Our approach may serve as an illustration of the role played by informed guesswork in research. First, we imagined that the mitotic apparatus was composed of proteins, an assumption for which there was slight factual basis. The cell generally employs proteins in the establishment of structure, and especially does so in the elaboration of fibrous structures. How are protein fibers formed and what are their properties? One mechanism of fiber formation is the establishment of the so-called disulfide (S-S) bridges between molecules. Protein molecules contain sulfur in the form of sulfhydryl (SH) groups. If, on two adjacent protein units, the hydrogens are removed (which is another way of saying that oxidation has occurred), the sulfur atoms of the two molecules may be linked in a disulfide bridge. Thus may fibrous chains be formed.

The disulfide bonds are very strong, so it is difficult to dissolve structures formed by them. In 1935 David Goddard and the late Leonor Michaelis, working at the Rockefeller Institute for Medical Research, showed that the reason why wool and similar proteins were so stable and insoluble in chemical solution was because they contained so many disulfide bridges. If, by the addition of an agent such as thioglycolic acid, the disulfide bonds were converted back to sulfhydryl bonds (a reversal of the oxidation described above), wool became soluble.

What does all this have to do with the mitotic apparatus? If the apparatus dissolves in Duponol or other strong detergents, the logical conclusion would be that the fibers of the spindle and asters are *not* formed by disulfide bridges. We drew the less logical conclusion that there were too few disulfide bridges to make the fibers sufficiently resistant. We then guessed—there is no other word that would be entirely honest—that there might be a larger number of *potential* disulfide bridges (SH groups) which could be converted to actual bridges (S-S bonds) by the addition of an oxidizing agent. On this assumption we treated the eggs briefly with a solution of hydrogen peroxide before adding the detergent.

The experiment—every step of which was based on inference as to how the cell *might* make the fibers of the mitotic apparatus— worked. The detergent dispersed everything in the cell except the mitotic apparatus, which was left intact! The contaminants could then be removed by letting the heavier mitotic apparatus settle out under a small centrifugal force. By repeated washing in this manner, a sediment composed of "pure" mitotic apparatus could be collected. The method set no limits on the number of dividing cells that could be used; it was possible to isolate enough of the mitotic apparatus for relatively large-scale chemical analysis.

The microscopic study of the isolated mitotic apparatus immediately supplies interesting information. Whatever the stage of mitosis, the whole apparatus may be isolated in one piece containing all the elements that entered into the description of mitosis. This proves that the cell does make a physically integrated apparatus for carrying out the cell-division process. An interesting result is obtained where one isolates the mitotic apparatus from clam eggs or other cells which do not divide into daughter cells of equal size. In these cases the asters are also of unequal size, the larger aster being at the end where the larger cell will form. Thus observations of isolated mitotic figures confirm Dan's theory as to how the plane of cell division is located. In general, observations of the isolated mitotic figures confirm the picture that had been obtained by earlier microscopists, but everything is much clearer and observation does not depend upon violent killing and staining procedures. The most interesting result of observing the isolated figures is the fact that they are isolated at all. This signifies that the dividing cell performs some chemical act, common to all parts of the apparatus, that makes it chemically different from everything else either in the dividing or the resting cell. This is a logical consequence of the fact that the isolation procedure works. While the procedure does not solve the "secret" of mitosis, it assures us at least that there is one, and one that can now be studied.

We now know something about the chemistry of the apparatus. It is composed mostly of protein, as was originally guessed. There is present a small amount of ribonucleic acid, and, of course, the contents of the chromosomes. Other constituents are suspected but not yet proved. The "weight" of a single mitotic apparatus has been determined: it is found that the apparatus involves about 2 per cent of all the protein in the egg at the time of its first division. This will certainly vary as cells of different kinds are investigated.

To what extent was the guess that the mitotic apparatus is formed by the linking together of protein molecules through sulfur bridges a legitimate one? A logical way to test this is by attempting to reverse the process. If the guesses were accurate—and the success of an experiment does not in itself prove that the assumptions which led to it were correct—then the mitotic apparatus should become soluble in detergent if the S-S bridges were reduced to unlinked SH groups. The experiment would be comparable to that by Goddard and Michaelis on the solubility of wool. The same reagent, thioglycolic acid, was used—and the predicted results were obtained. After treatment with this reagent, the mitotic apparatus was soluble in detergent. Therefore the idea that the fibers are formed through sulfur bridges is a tenable one. Once the protein of the mitotic apparatus is in solution, further information may be obtained. By the use of the ultracentrifuge, which measures how fast molecules settle under very strong gravitational forces, one can observe the size of the molecules. It appears that most of the apparatus consists of molecules about the size of "ordinary" proteins, such as the albumin of egg white. This might be considered the unit which the cell strings out by sulfur bridges to form the fibers of the mitotic apparatus.

While much could be learned from the mitotic apparatus isolated by peroxide and Duponol, the method was still a rough one. By the standards of the biochemist, peroxide is a rather violent reagent, and the isolation involved the creation of unnatural sulfur bridges which did not exist in the original cells. Following the same line of reasoning, now fortified by experiment, the problem could be simplified. If the "natural" mitotic apparatus depended upon disulfide bridges but contained relatively few, could we not use a detergent that was just strong enough to solubilize the other materials of the cell and just weak enough *not* to solubilize the mitotic apparatus? If such a detergent were available the peroxide could be omitted and the whole treatment would be gentler. After some trials such a detergent was found. It is a natural detergent: digitonin, which is obtained from the common foxglove. George Wald of Harvard University had used this substance some years ago to solubilize the visual pigments of the eye without damaging them chemically. Recent experiments in our laboratory have shown that digitonin alone will disperse the cell content and liberate the mitotic apparatus.

There is every reason to think that the isolated mitotic apparatus is now closer to its natural condition. Its structure remains intact down to fine details. A merit of the newer method is that the chromosomes, which were often difficult to see when isolated by the old method, are preserved. But again we must raise the question: was the reasoning that led to the successful isolation correct? If it was, the isolated mitotic apparatus could have fewer S-S groups and still be more soluble in thioglycolate than was the apparatus prepared by the old method. This proved to be the case.

Now a new and challenging fact emerges. Let us consider, for this soon becomes the heart of the problem, how the beautiful geometry of the mitotic apparatus might be achieved. On visual evidence alone the old masters of microscopy believed that the centrioles were in fact centers which formed the fibers of the mitotic apparatus. Since the appearance of these bodies varies so much from cell to cell, let us use the general term "center." The fibers do seem to grow out of the centers. No alternative hypothesis has been proposed, although it is often suggested that one group of fibers, those connecting the chromosomes to the poles, may originate in the chromosomes. Translating into chemical language, we may set up the working hypothesis that the form of the mitotic apparatus is determined by centers at which fibers are made by a process involving the formation of disulfide bonds. The peculiarity of these centers would be that they provide conditions favoring such a polymerization. Recent observations on the mitotic apparatus isolated by the digitonin method lend some support to such a line of thought. If the mitotic apparatus is given a very mild exposure to thioglycolic acid, everything dissolves but the spherical central region of the asters. This seems to be in fact the region where the S-S bridging of the proteins is strongest. We are a long way from understanding how the mitotic apparatus is formed, but the availability of the isolated apparatus and now the isolated centers should permit us to feed chemical information into the theory of mitosis as it evolves.

Mitosis cannot be understood merely as a series of chemical transformations. It is a dynamic mechanical process, a matter of push and pull, stress and strain. What tools have we to study this aspect of the problem? The most refined tool, and one that is being used most effectively, is the so-called polarization microscope. Where molecules are oriented, and take on other than random arrangements, they influence the speed and direction of beams of polarized light passing through them. The orientation may be the result of the architectural operations of the cell, as in the formation of the mitotic apparatus, or the result of mechanical stresses. The influence of an object composed of oriented units on a beam of polarized light is measured as its birefringence. Birefringence is actually the difference between the speed of a beam of polarized light through the object when the light waves are vibrating parallel to an axis of the object, and the speed of a beam vibrating at right angles to this axis. The axes are obvious in the case of an object such as an elongated fiber. What is important is that the birefringence may measure the degree of orderliness in the arrangement of the molecules or the extent to which the molecules themselves are nonsymmetrical. In the case of a fiber composed of long and slender units, the birefringence will increase if all the molecules are made to lie parallel to one another. It will decrease if for any reason the individual molecules become shorter or fatter.

Researchers whose main interest has been the problem of mitosis have in recent years refined the polarization microscope to the point where we may now hope for a real surge of information about the arrangement of molecules in the mitotic apparatus. A few examples will illustrate the kinds of information that we can expect. Some years ago a German pioneer in the field, W. J. Schmidt, showed that the mitotic spindle was birefringent, and that the birefringence decreased when the chromosomes were separating. This demonstrated that the fiber system of the spindle had as its basis a system of fibers of molecular dimensions, aligned more or less parallel to the visible fibers. The decrease in birefringence indicated either that fewer of the molecules were aligned along the axis of the spindle or that the molecules were contracting. Schmidt's methods were not sufficiently sensitive to detect small-scale changes. Recently Swann and Mitchison have refined the microscope so that much smaller degrees of birefringence can be measured, and the measurement can be made on a movie of the dividing sea-urchin egg. They were able to show that the decrease in birefringence as the chromosomes moved apart was not uniform, but began near the chromosomes and spread toward the poles. Swann has proposed that the changes that take place in the spindle during chromosome separation are initiated by one or more substances produced by the chromosomes. An engaging feature of this hypothesis is the way in which it demonstrates how a few facts (even when incorporated into a hypothesis that is difficult to prove) may resolve a seeming contradiction. For years cytologists have debated whether the chromosomes are pulled toward the poles or themselves provide the momentum for their migration. Swann's experiment reveals that both the spindle and the chromosomes may play an active part. This is often the outcome of such "either-or" controversies.

Microscopic research on mitosis has been both stimulated and plagued by debates as to whether this or that part of the mitotic apparatus was real or was an "artifact" produced by the technique of preparing the cell for observation. At one time the reality of even the chromosomes was debated; the question of their existence was only resolved by the ultimate court of appeal—observation in the living state. The controversy as to the reality of the fibers in the mitotic apparatus has continued to rage, though observations of the fibers in living cells have been reported by Kenneth Cooper of the University of Rochester and by others. In the opinion of the writer, the polarization microscope has solved this problem. Shinya Inoué, a young graduate student working under Cooper at Princeton University, designed and built a polarization microscope capable of detecting and measuring smaller degrees of birefringence than had previously been possible in biological material. With this instrument he has studied the mitotic figures in many kinds of living cells, and in every case he has been able to detect distinct spindle fibers. The fibers, which contrast so poorly with the background material in ordinary light, stand out vividly in polarized light by virtue of the arrangement of the molecules in them.

The reader is sure to ask about the contributions of the electron microscope to the study of mitosis. Living material cannot be examined in this instrument because the beam of electrons with which it resolves very small objects must be focused in a vacuum. Thus the application of the electron microscope to the study of mitosis is already beset by arguments as to whether the observations made with it are real or artifacts.

The difficulties could have been predicted from the troubles of pre-electron microscopists. "Seeing" depends on contrast, and the electron microscope, however great its magnifying power, depends on a rather high degree of contrast (difference in density of matter between an object and its surroundings) in order to show an object at all. It is perhaps for this reason that the mitotic apparatus, observed while it was embedded in the other constituents of the cell, has seemed so structureless even to skilled electron microscopists. On the other hand, the isolated mitotic apparatus promises to show a great deal of structure. Patricia Harris of our laboratory has made photographs of the isolated mitotic apparatus which, even at the relatively low powers employed thus far, reveal a number of interesting details. It seems, for example, that the spindle fibers are not straight and continuous from pole to pole, but appear to be formed by an end-to-end union of fibers from either pole at the equator. As everyone would have predicted, the fibrous appearance of the spindle is not due to distinct fibers with nothing between them; the spindle is more like a sheaf of threads with a tendency to lie side by side. What will be seen as the full resolving power of the electron microscope is brought into play cannot yet be predicted. So powerful is this tool that we are forced to proceed slowly toward the highest magnifications, using each step to provide the landmarks for the next.

If we survey the whole living world, we see that mitosis is the most common mechanism for distributing the hereditary birthright, and the most fundamental features of mitosis are the formation of a "plate" of doubled chromosomes and the formation of a spindle which will guide each of the daughters of chromosome doubling to the opposite pole. There are important exceptions to this typical pattern. In the growth of our own muscles, for example, nuclei may reproduce by mitosis without the formation of new cells around them. Growth keeps pace with the number of nuclei, and the result is huge cells with many nuclei. There are instances where, after the division of nuclei alone has given rise to a large cell, the cell suddenly builds a wall around each nucleus so that we end up, after all, with as many cells as there are nuclei. This process is of great practical importance, for the formation of infectious spores in many microorganisms is due to it. How new cells can be marked out without a mitotic apparatus to guide the process we do not understand at all.

As mentioned earlier, we cannot detect asters in many cells, especially those of plants. Nor have the centers toward which the chromosomes of plants migrate been identified visually as the distinct bodies called centrioles. In some very common instances, such as the division of white blood cells and other cells that crawl like amoebae, the division is accompanied by lively movements. Such divisions look for all the world as though, once the forming daughter cells decide that they are daughter cells, they try to crawl away from their sisters and thus aid the division process. In many but not all of the protozoa, the one-celled animals, there is a peculiar kind of mitosis in which the nuclear surface does not break down. The spindle forms inside the nucleus, which elongates as the daughter chromosomes part, and finally pinches in two. Even here, where we can see neither asters nor mitotic apparatus outside the nucleus, the cell "knows" where the equator of the peculiar spindle is, for it pinches into two at the midpoint. We also have, in such diverse instances as mosquito gut cells and certain plant cells, "endomitosis," which involves neither cell division nor even the separation of the daughter chromosomes into new nuclei. The chromosomes simply divide and remain together in the same nucleus.

The advance of biology is an interplay of generalization and exception, and attitudes toward exceptions tell us more about biologists than they do about biology. To the writer it seems that the diverse patterns of cell multiplication will emerge as variations on a simple design once we learn something of what lies beneath the surface.

In the full context of nature the biological world is characterized by continuous growth, limited only by the resources and hazards of the physical world. But, just as human beings fancy themselves as being more than mere descendants and ancestors, so the life of an organism is largely a vacation from the propagation of its kind. Even single cells do not add to their store of living matter during division, but only between divisions. In higher organisms the pattern of development is a counterpoint of division and organization. In the embryo the frequency of mitosis decreases before the forms and specializations of the adult come into being. When a group of cells reverses this pattern, we have a cancer. What sets mitosis into motion and what stops it? We have only a few scattered facts to marshal against these questions. In general, the mass of a cell must reach a critical maximum value before it begins to divide. If we keep amputating part of an amoeba so that it never reaches full size, it never divides. We also have learned in the last few years that mitosis is a process which distributes equally between the daughter cells chromosomes which have doubled before mitosis begins. It is conceivable that the control of mitosis involves restraints on the synthesis of new chromosome material.

What artificial restraints can we place on mitosis, short of simply murdering cells? We know several kinds. One is to suppress the synthesis of the nucleic acids of the chromosomes. This is what happens when we expose cells to mild doses of X-rays or other ironizing radiation from which they generally recover. Heavier doses of radiation upset mitosis by breaking up the chromosomes. So far as we know, most biological effects of radiation involve the formation and the integrity of the chromosomes. Chemicals that duplicate these effects are called radiomimetic—mimickers of radiation. On the other hand, ionizing radiation seems to have little effect on the mitotic apparatus apart from the chromosomes, but many chemicals do. Substances such as the plant derivative colchicine prevent the formation of the mitotic spindle, but do not affect the chromosomes. The chromosomes go through their complete mitotic cycle, but cannot be separated because there is no mitotic apparatus. The result is a single cell with a double portion of chromosomes. Such antimitotic agents have been used successfully in the palliation, but not the cure, of cancer, and have been useful where it was desirable to breed organisms such as food plants with twice the parental ration of chromosomes. It goes without saying that a reasonable approach to the problem of controlling mitosis will depend on understanding mitosis itself.

Biology has few generalizations that can be dignified by the word "law," and to most of these there are exceptions. But no exception has been discovered to the law that every cell must arise from another cell. This generalization makes sense once we have discovered the essential accomplishment of mitosis: the deployment of the chromosomes so that each daughter cell is assured a full representation of all the chromosomes in the mother cell.

The essential meaning of mitosis can be learned from microscopic observation alone, and was learned many years ago. Now we begin to see some progress toward a deeper understanding of what actually is happening in the dividing cell. Through the combined efforts of those who study virus reproduction and those who investigate cell division, we may hope to have some insight into the mechanism whereby the chromosome material is duplicated before mitosis begins. But there are aspects of the mitotic process that do not lend themselves so well to analysis by current means. Should we ask how the chromosomes come to align themselves in the correct geometric plane before they separate and how sister chromosomes find their way to opposite poles, we discover that we are dealing with an order of problems that does not fit into current methods or ways of thinking about biological events. While we are learning a great deal about the chemistry of cells, we are a long way from understanding how any part of the cell knows where it is.

CELL DIFFERENTIATION
by C. H. Waddington

How is it that a single fertilized egg, a tiny blob of apparently formless protoplasm, can become a man—with eyes, ears, arms, legs, heart and brain? How from one generalized cell do we get the myriad of different specialized cells that make a human body? This puzzle, differentiation, is of course one of the great questions of biology. The process of differentiation has always seemed particularly mysterious because there are so few phenomena in the nonliving world that might give us clues as to how it takes place. In the inanimate realm we do not often come across a situation in which parts of a single mass of material gradually diverge from one another and become completely distinct in character. Yet in all living things, except perhaps the viruses, differentiation is a basic law of nature.

For half a century biologists have been searching for the answers to this question by two main methods of attack: the modern sciences of embryology and genetics. On one hand they have been investigating directly by experiment how the embryo develops, and on the other they have studied how the genes control the processes of development. Let us start with the embryological approach.

The problem was bogged down for a long time in a debate between two theories first described by Aristotle in the fourth century B.C. One school argued that the newly fertilized egg contains all the organs of the animal in miniature, and that these preformed parts merely grow and enlarge to produce the adult. The second view, supported by Aristotle, was that the organs are formed only gradually by interaction among simple parts or constituents of the

210

egg. Aristotle called this process "epigenesis," and epigenetics is still an appropriate name for the embryological approach to the problem.

When modern investigators began to experiment on animal embryos, they seemed to find support for both of the ancient theories. They cut an egg of a simple animal in half, or removed a part of the egg, and let the remaining part develop. In some types of animals, the fragment of egg developed into an adult with certain parts missing, which suggested that the egg contained preformed and rather rigidly localized rudiments of the adult organs. On the other hand, in other cases a complete and normal adult grew from the amputated egg. It was clear that epigenetic interactions must have taken place in these eggs.

The first experimenter to carry out a controlled study of such interactions was the German embryologist Hans Spemann, of the little Black Forest town of Freiburg. He operated on early embryos of the common newt. As the eggs of this animal develop, the first visible structure to appear is a small depression, called the blastopore, which eventually will become the main part of the intestine. Spemann cut out the region of the blastopore from one egg and grafted it into a second egg in a different position. There it not only continued to develop but influenced the cells surrounding it. They then became the main organs of the embryo, e.g., the central nervous system and the rudiments of the spinal column.

Here was a clear-cut case of exactly the kind of interaction suggested by the epigenetic theory. Spemann called the blastopore region the "organizer" of the embryo. Soon organizers very similar to the one he had discovered in his salamander were found in many other classes of vertebrate animals. Such organizers were found to be responsible for the formation not only of the main embryonic axis but of many secondary organs which arise rather later: the ear, the nose, the lens of the eye, and so on. Sometimes the organizer region is relatively sharply demarcated and precisely localized. In other eggs it may be more diffuse, and the interactions may take place in a graded way, one end of the region being more powerful than the other. But in either case, the development of organs is determined by the interaction between some dominant part of the egg and its more receptive surroundings.

Now an organ has two aspects. It consists in the first place of specific types of tissue, which can come into being only by differentiation of the cells. But further than that, the tissues in an organ are arranged in certain relations to one another that give the organ its characteristic shape. Of course in the last analysis the shape of an organ presumably is an expression of the nature of the tissues composing it, but it is convenient to make a rough distinction between the formation of specific tissues and the molding of these tissues into organic structures. Most recent work has concentrated on the first of these problems: the nature of the chemical processes by which the embryonic cells become differentiated.

It was natural to suppose at first that the organizer could act only as a living entity. But in 1932 it was discovered that an organizer is able to influence its surroundings even after it has been killed! This discovery was made simultaneously in the newt embryo by a group of German workers including Johannes Holtfreter (who is now at the University of Rochester) and in the chick embryo by myself at Cambridge University. It seemed that we might be on the verge of a critically important advance: that the influence of the organizer on development might be traced to some chemical substance which could be extracted from it. Several groups of workers tried to identify the substance, but their hopes were too optimistic and their picture of the situation too simple. The trouble is not in finding a substance that will act like the organizer in inducing cellular differentiation but that *too many* substances will do just that. Within a year or two Joseph Needham, Jean Brachet and I had proved conclusively that methylene blue, a substance which cannot by any stretch of the imagination be supposed to exist in the normal embryo, will bring about the formation of nerve tissue when injected into the embryo. It seems

212

useless to look for some master substance in the cells which will give us the key to the understanding of differentiation. The place to study differentiation is in the reacting tissue, which actually carries out the differentiation. Only during a certain period of development is this tissue able to react to the organizer stimulus; it is then said to be "competent." The way to a deeper insight into the nature of development is through a fuller understanding of competence.

It is here that the hereditary genes come into the picture. In all likelihood the competence of the cell for differentiation is a complex state of affairs, involving many different chemical systems. We know that there are many genes in the nucleus of a cell and that each gene controls the formation of one or more of the substances produced as the cell develops. Thus the set of gene-controlled processes must be the system of reactions involved in the state of competence.

The most obvious question to ask is: What is the nature of each individual gene reaction? But, before considering that, there is another point which may be almost as important and is perhaps easier to approach. We are dealing with a complex system of reactions, one starting from each gene, and finishing up with all the numerous constituents of an adult tissue. Do any general features characterize the system as a whole?

There is one important general feature. An adult animal consists of a number of different organs and tissues which are sharply bounded off from one another. The liver does not merge gradually into the pancreas and that into some other organ. Cells develop into one type or the other; they do not form graded intermediates. Further, there is a strong tendency for these normal end-products to be produced even if conditions during development have been somewhat abnormal. We can, for instance, cut pieces out of the embryo or cause other experimental alterations, and the embryo will still produce a normal adult.

This means that development must be organized into a number

of distinct systems. One system of processes will bring about the development of, say, the nervous tissue. A different system will produce liver or kidney or some other tissue of the body. Moreover, each system must be stabilized in some way so that it gives its normal end-product even if it has to go by an unusual way to get there.

This shows us the kinds of facts we have to account for. One of the great tasks for embryology in the immediate future is to explore the ways in which systems with properties of this kind can arise. There are several different ways by which we could seek to account for the fact that development is channeled into separate, distinct pathways. For instance, if the product of the reaction itself makes the reaction go faster—that is to say, if the processes are autocatalytic—it is easy to see that once a process has begun to form a particular product, that product will encourage the process to go still further in the same direction, and thus exclude any other possible product. Similarly, if the product of one reaction inhibits the progress of some other reaction, then as soon as the first process gets under way it will tend to prevent the second from occurring. Common sense is enough to offer certain general suggestions of this kind, but we badly need a thorough theoretical study of the various conceivable types of interaction between processes. Beyond that, we need an experimental analysis of developmental processes, aimed at discovering which of the theoretical possibilities are realized in practice.

For the self-regulating feature of the embryo's development, we can find models in the field of engineering: automatic ships' compasses, automatic pilots and other feedback mechanisms for which the name of cybernetics has recently become fashionable. In cell differentiation we must be dealing with chemical cybernetic systems. The properties of biological enzymes should make it possible for such systems to be built up in several different ways, but we still know remarkably little about them. Very probably much of the work required to understand these systems will be done on systems of isolated chemical substances which may at first sight seem to have little or nothing to do with embryology.

I have found it helpful to make a mechanical picture of the set of differentiation systems, each of which leads to one definite end-result and is balanced internally by some sort of cybernetic mechanism. Let us imagine the cells as a group of balls perched on the top of a slope. On this slope we may suppose there is a radiating system of valleys. As each ball rolls down, it must pass into one valley or another. Once it has started down a given valley, its fate (the end-product it will become) is determined, for it will be very unlikely to roll over the intervening hill into another valley, and even if some abnormal condition temporarily pushes it part way up the bank, it will tend, like a bobsled, to slide back to the bottom of its chute and continue its normal course. I have used the name "epigenetic landscape" for this picture of the developing system.

Our other principal task is a detailed study of the chemical processes that go on in a cell as it moves from its embryonic beginnings to its final differentiated state. When it was discovered that many substances could act like the organizer to induce differentiations, most people argued that they must be acting in a secondary way. Suppose that all the cells of the embryo contain some substance which can induce the formation of, for instance, nervous tissue. Suppose further that in most cases this substance is concealed or inactivated, but that it can be liberated by certain types of cell metabolism. Then one would expect that the organizer gets its peculiar properties from its specific metabolism. Following this line of thought, several groups of investigators have measured the metabolism of the organizer against that of other regions of the egg. They have duly found that the organizer has certain special metabolic characteristics, and it is quite clear that these are essentially involved in its developmental activity. For instance, in the eggs of the sea urchin the fundamental developmental system consists of two gradients of activity, one of which is most powerful at the upper end of the egg, the other at the lower end. The thing that varies along these gradients is the intensity of processes of cellular metabolism, and on these variations depends the differentiation of the parts of the egg.

Eggs and embryos are, of course, exceedingly small things, and the technical difficulty of studying the metabolism of parts of the egg is very large indeed. Some subtle types of supersensitive apparatus have been worked out which enable one to operate with minute quantities of material. One of the most refined is the well-known Cartesian diver. This old toy, which apparently has nothing to do with the French philosopher Descartes, after whom it is named, is a tiny vessel of thin glass with an open neck. In this neck a drop of oil is placed and the whole thing is immersed in a flask of water. As the diver sinks below the water surface, the pressure of water from above forces down the oil drop, compresses the air in the vessel into a smaller volume and so makes the glass bubble sink further. It can be made to float at a predetermined level, however, by adjusting the atmospheric pressure on the surface of the water in the flask. If now we have inside the stabilized diver a small piece of tissue which is using up oxygen or giving out carbon dioxide, this will alter the volume of the gas inside the diver and thus affect its buoyancy. This change can be measured by altering the atmospheric pressure until the diver just floats at its original level. The apparatus provides an exceedingly sensitive method of measuring minute changes in gas volume; with it one can measure respirations which involve as little as one millionth of a cubic centimeter of gas.

With such instruments we have acquired in the last few years a large amount of information about the respiration of various parts of the egg and other aspects of metabolism which are technically easy to measure. Unfortunately these processes are not always the kinds that seem most likely to lead to an understanding of cell differentiation. Differentiated cells probably are distinguished from one another principally by their protein constituents. We still know exceedingly little about how proteins are

216

formed, and biochemical investigation of protein production in embryos has not yet made much progress.

Like so many projects in biology, this investigation may turn largely on finding a suitable experimental material. The whole of embryology suffers at present from operating too much in terms of complex entities. Instead of considering the development of nervous tissue or liver tissue, each of which contains many substances, we must be able to investigate the development of some single substance. Again, instead of thinking in terms of transplanting lumps of material from one part of the embryo to the other, we shall have to start experimenting on the constituents of a single cell. We have as yet no good material in which we can follow quantitatively the synthesis of some specific protein and investigate the effect of various conditions on this process.

The genetic study of development is not open to this reproach. In genetics we can easily study one kind of unit involved in development, namely the gene. One of the most important things that has been going on in genetics recently is the attempt to connect individual genes with the specific single substances for whose production they are responsible. As the work reported in this book by George Beadle indicates, in microorganisms such as yeasts or fungi, which have a very simple body and a somewhat simpler biochemical system than more complicated animals, a change in a single gene often produces an obvious alteration in only one chemical constituent. Frequently this constituent is an enzyme, that is to say, one of the biological catalysts on which the functioning of the cell depends. It is probable, indeed, that all genes exert their influence through enzymes, and data from microorganisms suggest that each gene has an effect on a particular enzyme. If this is so, it would be logical to suppose that the gene manufactures the enzyme. It is not by any means certain that the matter is really as simple as all that. There may be several steps between the gene and the enzyme, in which case a number of different substances would be involved. We should then be dealing with a

217

chemical system not very different from the one discussed in connection with the competence of embryonic tissues.

From the point of view of cell differentiation, however, this work in microbiology is not so helpful as one might think. The microorganisms are the very creatures that show the least amount of differentiation. Genes exercise their control, it is generally believed, by interacting in different ways with different regions of the cytoplasm in the egg. In microorganisms there is little or no specialization of different regions of cytoplasm, so we cannot hope to get from them any direct information about this fundamental relationship between genes and cytoplasm.

We have, however, found some valuable indirect clues. It has been known for some time that a strain of yeast growing in a sugar solution will often develop the ability to ferment that type of sugar although it could not do so originally. It forms what is known as an adaptive enzyme for doing so. Biochemists and geneticists have learned that in general a strain of yeast can form an adaptive enzyme to a particular sugar only if it has a hereditary capacity to do so. In other words, the forming of an adaptive enzyme depends on the presence of the appropriate gene. This gene must, however, be activated by the presence of the sugar. The situation is an extraordinary parallel to what we imagine must happen when specific genes are activated in certain cytoplasmic regions of the egg. Since each adaptive enzyme is a specific protein, we have here an opportunity to study quantitatively the physical and chemical factors involved in protein synthesis. Sir Cyril Hinshelwood at Oxford University, Sol Spiegelman at the University of Illinois, Jacques Monod in Paris and others are already pursuing this line of inquiry.

From this protein study has come the stimulating suggestion that between the gene and the final enzyme there may be intermediates which, once formed, can reproduce themselves, for some time at least, even if the gene that produced them is removed. Several authors recently have come to the conclusion, some rather hastily, that they had evidence for the existence of such substances,

218

and they have given them a variety of names—plasmagenes, cyto-
genes and so on. In several cases further investigation showed
either that the evidence was not as good as had been thought or
that the suggested plasmagenes were actually foreign virus particles or something of a similar nature. In a certain number of cases,
however, there is fairly convincing evidence for the existence of
plasmagene-like bodies. One of the best known is found in the
little Paramecium. In this single-celled organism the cell develops
certain substances which can be recognized by the fact that they
stimulate the production of specific antibodies when they are injected into rabbits. The development of each substance is controlled by a corresponding plasmagene. The plasmagenes again
are under the control of nuclear genes, and the nucleus itself is
influenced by the condition of the cytoplasm of the cell. The cytoplasmic state can be altered by growing the animals at different
temperatures or by changing their environment in other ways.
Each cytoplasmic condition activates a certain gene to manufacture its corresponding plasmagene, and that in turn produces the
final cell constituent.

It seems likely that something similar goes on in embryonic development. The different regions of the egg can be supposed to
activate particular groups of genes in the nuclei which enter them;
the activated genes then control the differentiation of cells. The
first step in this will be the production of immediate gene products which may or may not be endowed with the power of self-
reproduction, like plasmagenes. The Belgian embryologist Brachet
has argued that certain minute particles which can be discovered
in cells, the so-called microsomes, are the actual plasmagenes.
These particles, just barely visible under ordinary microscopes,
can be separated from the rest of the cell by ultracentrifugation.
Brachet supposes that they are the immediate agents of protein
synthesis in the cytoplasm, operating under the ultimate control
of the nuclear genes. There is as yet no absolutely convincing proof
of this. We badly need to develop techniques for investigating
more thoroughly the relation between these microsomes and the

nucleus, for instance by isolating the microsomes from one cell and transplanting them into another whose development would normally be different.

The gene-plasmagene and gene-microsome story is the place at which the two sciences of genetics and embryology are coming together most closely. It also introduces the last pair of actors in our account. These are the two nucleic acids, usually known as DNA (desoxyribonucleic acid) and RNA (ribonucleic acid). They are always present in those parts of the cell most deeply involved in the production of new substances, and it seems most probable that nucleic acid of one kind or the other is essential for the production of any protein. There seems to be no doubt that DNA, a constituent of the chromosomes that house the genes, must be in some way closely connected with the genes themselves, which contain protein. RNA always occurs in high concentration in any region of cytoplasm in which rapid synthesis of proteins is proceeding. The microsomes, for instance, contain large quantities of RNA but little or no DNA. According to one present theory, the DNA-containing chromosomes manufacture RNA, which passes out of the nucleus into the cytoplasm and there becomes attached to the microsomes and takes part in the synthesis of the cellular proteins.

Here again we are standing on the challenging frontier of unexplored territory. We may flatter ourselves that we are converging on the secret of differentiation from all sides, but the advances we have made so far do more to reveal the extent of the area still to be explored than to provide satisfying explanations. The older surgical methods of experimental embryology and the general genetical studies have given us some clues as to the over-all nature of the system we are dealing with. But they emphasize, on the one hand, the need for developing a broad picture of it and, on the other, the importance of getting down to concrete chemical detail. Thus every part of the advancing front of knowledge must look for support to every other, and the order of the day all along the line must be to press on.

PART 6 MUSCLE, NERVE AND BRAIN

I. MUSCLE RESEARCH
by A. Szent-Györgyi

In the U. S. since 1947, Albert Szent-Györgyi carries on his important investigation of the physiology and biochemistry of muscle action at the Institute for Muscle Research, organized around his work at Woods Hole, Massachusetts. He was born in Budapest, Hungary, in 1893, and received his degree in medicine from the University of Budapest. Szent-Györgyi was awarded the Nobel prize in medicine for 1937. Before coming to the U. S. he taught and did research at the universities of Szeged and Budapest.

II. NERVE IMPULSE
by Bernhard Katz

Head of the Biophysics Department at University College, London, Bernhard Katz is one of the world's leading investigators of the electrochemistry of the nerve impulse. He was born in Australia in 1911, received an M.D. at the University of Leipzig and a Ph.D. at University College. In World War II, he flew with the Royal Australian Air Force in the Pacific Theater with the rank of Flight Lieutenant. Katz was elected a Fellow of the Royal Society in 1952.

III. THE ELECTRICAL ACTIVITY OF THE BRAIN
by W. Grey Walter

A British physiologist, W. Grey Walter, has demonstrated an unusual knack for electronics in the development of instrumentation for study of the function of the brain. He pioneered the research uses of the electroencephalograph, developed "Topsy," an array of cathode-ray tubes for presentation of a topographical pattern of the electrical activity in the brain described in this chapter, and designed *Machina speculatrix* and *Machina docilis*, two species of robots that simulate the choosing and learning aspects of animal behavior. Now forty-three years old, Walter has pursued his studies for the past fifteen years at Burden Neurological Institute, Bristol, England. He is a prolific writer and lecturer on his subject, a popular broadcaster on BBC and author of *The Living Brain*.

MUSCLE RESEARCH

by A. Szent-Györgyi

WHEN one of our muscles is excited by a nerve it contracts. Some muscles are thus able to pull at the bones to which they are attached and to move a part of the body. Other muscles perform much of the work of our internal organs. The heart is only a pouch of muscle; so, in a way, are the intestines. Millions of muscle cells are embedded in the walls of small arteries.

Much of human suffering is due to the disfunction of these inner muscles. A slight contraction of the muscles of the arteries may send the blood pressure up or cut off the supply of oxygen to other tissues. More than half the deaths of mankind are due to the failure of heart muscle. Yet in most cases we cannot repair the diseased muscle machine because we do not sufficiently understand its structure and function.

Muscular contraction is one of the most wonderful phenomena of the biological kingdom. That a soft jelly should suddenly become hard, change its shape and lift a thousand times its own weight, and that it should be able to do so several hundred times a second, is little short of miraculous. Undoubtedly muscle is one of the most remarkable items in nature's curiosity shop. Muscle, however, has attracted the attention of many scientific investigators for another reason.

All living organisms are but leaves on the same tree of life. The various functions of plants and animals and their specialized organs are manifestations of the same living matter. This adapts itself to different jobs and circumstances, but operates on the same basic principles. Muscle contraction is only one of these adapta-

223

tions. In principle it would not matter whether we studied nerve, kidney or muscle to understand the basic principles of life. In practice, however, it matters a great deal.

The work of the scientist is essentially to measure, and the rapid changes in muscle can be measured much more easily than the slow changes in liver or kidney. The functioning of muscle may be seen by the naked eye, and may be indicated by simple means. The electrical change of nerve, on the other hand, may be observed only with involved and subtle devices. The great motility of muscle demands that it be built of small units, arranged with great regularity and bound together by relatively weak forces. This means that we may disentangle and isolate these small units without destroying them, and that they may be studied outside the body.

There are many approaches to the study of muscle. The anatomist delights in its structure, which he tries to preserve. The physiologist enjoys the harmony of its function, and tries to avoid all damage to the tissue in order to study it under physiological conditions. The biochemist, however, willfully destroys the structure. There is a simple reason for the fact that none of these approaches, in itself, can explain muscle.

Muscle is a machine, and in any machine we must deal with two elements. One is the energy-yielding reaction, such as the expansion of steam in a steam engine, the burning of fuel in an internal combustion engine, or the flow of current in an electric motor. These elementary reactions can accomplish useful work only if they take place within a specific structure, be it a cylinder and a piston or a coil and a rotor. So in muscle we must also look for both the energy-yielding reaction and the meaningful structure.

The energy-yielding reaction is a chemical change which takes place among molecules, and its study belongs to the realm of biochemistry. The structure is the domain of the anatomist, working with his knife, microscope or electron microscope. Both paths of inquiry are most exciting. We can expect to find that the basic energy-yielding reaction is identical, at least in principle, in all living forms. Muscle research can thus take us to the very foundation of life. Its structure, although specialized, can likewise reveal the fundamental principles of biomolecular architecture. In this light muscle ceases to be a special problem. The study of its function merges with the study of all life, and for such study muscle is a wonderful and unique material.

Muscle is built of tiny fibers which are just visible to the naked eye. If we look at one of these under the microscope, we see a pattern of horizontal striations which indicates that the muscle fiber itself is a bundle of many smaller fibers, or fibrils. These fibrils are composed of contractile matter, and the muscle fiber contracts because the fibrils contract.

The fibrils need a great deal of energy in a very special form. The energy contained in food, in fact, must be converted into this form before the fibrils can use it. This process alone requires a bulky chemical apparatus that is located between the fibrils. The contraction of the fibrils presses the substance of this chemical apparatus into disks, and it is the pattern of these disks between the fibrils that gives the muscle fiber its striated appearance. When the substance is removed and the fibril itself lies naked, we can see with the help of the electron microscope that it too is a bundle of still finer threads. These threads have been called filaments by C. A. Hall, M. A. Jacus and F. O. Schmitt, who first photographed them at the Massachusetts Institute of Technology.

The specific form in which energy is supplied to the fibril is adenosine triphosphate, which is abbreviated as ATP. The discovery of this substance is one of the most important achievements of biochemistry. ATP is one of the main axes about which life revolves. The ATP molecule bears three phosphate groups linked by oxygen atoms. The University of Pennsylvania physiologist O. Meyerhof has shown that the manufacture of each such link requires 11,000 calories of free energy. When the links are broken, the energy is released. Fritz Lipmann of the Massachusetts General Hospital has called them high-energy phosphate links. Their splitting is the source of all muscular energy.

The participation of ATP in contraction has one most fascinating aspect. Our experience thus far indicates that wherever there is life its carrier is a nucleoprotein. This substance is made up of protein and nucleic acid, the latter being most abundant in cell nuclei. We may therefore assume that these two materials and their interactions are an essential feature of life. The nucleic acid molecule is composed of many small units that are chemically similar to ATP. These are joined in giant fibrous molecules. Unfortunately we cannot do much with such large molecules, so they can tell us little of the nature and meaning of nucleoproteins.

Again muscle furnishes a hopeful exception. So far as the author is aware, the contractile substance of the fibrils is the only "living" protein that is not linked to nucleic acid. The reason is easy to find. Long, fibrous nucleic acid molecules would surely interfere with the mechanism of contraction. Instead of nucleic acid, the contractile protein works with smaller units. In the author's opinion, ATP is the missing nucleic acid of the fibril. Since ATP is a small molecule, its connection with muscle protein can be studied with relative ease, and may reveal one of life's most closely guarded secrets.

Having outlined some general principles, let us see what we can actually learn about the function of muscle. To understand it we will have to break it down. From a knowledge of its parts we may hope to understand the whole, just as the astronomer understands the stars by his knowledge of the atom. A man who parachuted into a strange land, however, might have difficulty in finding his way home. We would likewise have trouble finding our way back to muscle if we decomposed it all at once. We will fare better if we proceed to our destination on foot, and decompose muscle step by step.

As the first step in decomposing muscle, let us separate the small, soluble molecules from the insoluble structure without destroying the latter. This can easily be done by washing a strip of rabbit muscle, for example, with water. Now let us put the dissolved molecules back again. We suspend our muscle in a concentrate of the original solution, or, to simplify matters, in a boiled extract of some other muscle tissue. What happens? The muscle contracts! Special measurements show that the contraction occurred with such force that the muscle could have lifted a thousand times its own weight, just as any living muscle. There is no doubt that what we have seen is muscle contraction.

Next we ask: What substance in this muscle juice made the washed muscle contract? Fortunately this is not a difficult question. A bit of scientific cookery indicates that two substances were responsible—potassium and ATP. This is remarkable, for ATP is essentially phosphate, and if we want a lawn to flourish, we use a fertilizer containing potassium and phosphate. Grass needs the same substances as muscle, a striking demonstration that the basic change in muscle contraction is only one form of a universal biochemical reaction.

We have thus discovered that ATP makes muscle contract as well as supplying the energy for contraction. No other substance will serve. ATP is a cogwheel in the mechanism of contraction, and without it no contraction occurs. ATP has yet another function. From earliest times man has known of *rigor mortis,* the stiffening of the body that follows death. The same effect can be produced in a single muscle. A strip of rabbit muscle removed soon after killing the animal can be stretched like rubber, though within narrower limits. A few hours later the strip becomes inelastic and simply breaks when we attempt to stretch it. The loss of elasticity is due to the decomposition of ATP; by restoring ATP we restore elasticity. If ATP did not make muscle elastic, the muscle would be too rigid to work at all.

We can now go one step further in decomposing muscle. We make a very fine pulp of our washed rabbit muscle, suspend it in water and add potassium and ATP. No contraction can occur because the structures have been destroyed. Instead there is a

227

violent precipitation. Much the same thing must have happened when the whole muscle contracted. The precipitation of fine colloidal particles is due chiefly to a loss of electric charge. So the basic reaction of contraction is a loss of charge, brought about by potassium and ATP.

We may now proceed to decompose muscle into its molecules. In the presence of ATP a strong salt solution dissolves the muscle structure and extracts two quite different proteins—actin and myosin. Both of these proteins have most interesting properties, but contractility is not one of them. The most amazing property of myosin is its great affinity with ions, which in the smallest concentrations may greatly modify its electric charge. The most amazing property of actin, discovered by the author's associate F. B. Straub, is that it can exist in two forms. When first extracted it consists of small, round molecules. If we add a little salt these little globules unite to form long threads.

The most amazing property of actin and myosin, however, is that they can unite to form a complex—actomyosin. It is this complex that has the contractility of muscle. We have reproduced, and thus made it possible to analyze, one of the most mysterious manifestations of life. Seeing actomyosin contract for the first time was the most exciting experience of the author's scientific career.

We have left the problem of the molecular architecture of muscle to the end, because this field of research was opened not long ago when the discovery of the electron microscope extended the limit of human vision down to the world of molecules. Hall, Jacus and Schmitt were the first to begin studies along this line. At present the problem is also being investigated at the National Institute of Health by G. Rozsa, the author and R. W. G. Wyckoff, in the laboratory of the latter. These studies have shown that the building of actin out of globules into fibers proceeds in two steps. First perhaps 20 globules unite into a slightly elongated particle some 300 Angstrom units long and 100 wide. Then these particles are joined end to end to form threads. Electron-microscope photographs show that the threads have a strong tendency to come to rest side by side so that the individual particles of neighboring threads also lie side by side. Thus threads actually form in two directions, and a regular structure analogous to a crystal results.

The nature of the chemical mechanism that makes large protein molecules out of small ones is a very fascinating problem. The larger actin particles are the size of the smaller viruses. The question of how a large protein unit is put together, and how it is taken apart and put together again according to a new pattern, is perhaps the most important problem of virus research. W. J. Bowen and K. Laki of the National Institute of Health have shown that ATP is also involved in this feat of molecular engineering.

There is yet another new and rather hopeful approach to muscle, opened by the discovery that muscular contraction is a so-called equilibrium reaction. The approach is that of thermodynamics. It has thus far yielded two rather fascinating results. It has shown that the whole muscle machine is built of small and more or less independent units the size of actin globules. These have a molecular weight of 70,000, i.e., 70,000 times the weight of the hydrogen atom. If linked to ATP, the units at rest have a certain amount of potential energy, and are thus comparable to a loaded gun or an extended spring. When excited by a nervous impulse, the units spend this energy. The energy transmitted by ATP is then required to bring them back to the high-energy loaded or extended state. Once we know this, it seems natural that nature should do it this way. The living structure is kept ready to fire and is loaded after firing, instead of the other way around.

Can we put all this together in a single theory of muscle contraction? We can try, but we must jump some rather wide gaps. We have seen that the primary reaction is a change in which electric charge is lost, and that the change takes place within small molecular units. Such a loss of charge must very greatly alter the forces between the larger particles. Should it be found that the muscle fibril is a three-dimensional structure of slightly elongated

229

particles, it might also be found that contraction is nothing more than a tilting of them.

Much work must be done before we have a rounded understanding of muscle contraction itself. Then we must ask what changes occur when a nerve commands a muscle to contract, how the system returns to its resting state, and how the energy of ATP is transferred. Since actomyosin appears to be identical in all kinds of muscle, we will have to look out for the substances that regulate its varying functions. In the wing muscle of some insects, for example, actomyosin can contract several hundred times a second, yet it can also produce the slow, regular beat of the heart and, without consuming energy, can hold a clam shell closed for hours.

The reader may ask: When we know all this, will we understand muscle and life itself? The author can only give his personal opinion: We will not, because the fundamental changes in muscle cannot be expressed in terms of orthodox chemistry. We will very likely have to explain them in terms of how electrons are distributed over the entire molecular structure, an explanation that belongs to the realm of quantum mechanics.

The study of this distribution of electrons within the protein molecule is one of the most urgent and most difficult tasks of biology. Until the task has been completed, we cannot hope to understand the nature of life. The task is not impossible, but it requires keen imagination, a lust for adventure, and a catholic knowledge. The task is probably too big for any one man; the biologist and the theoretical physicist will have to collaborate. A few hopeful beginnings have been made. They may eventually lead us to a full understanding of the protein molecule, which will mark the beginning of a new era in biology and medicine.

NERVE IMPULSE
by Bernhard Katz

THE LIFE of an organism, like that of organized society, depends upon its system of communication. The remarkable instruments of communication that integrate our civilization—the telephone, telegraph, radio, television—are much less remarkable than the communications system that integrates a human being. Our nervous system has powerful transmitting equipment, sensitive receivers, trunk lines connecting distant points in the body, a central exchange which sorts and co-ordinates messages. It transmits messages to all parts of the body reliably and rapidly—often in a small fraction of a second. Yet nature has managed to produce this elaborate and efficient signaling system in a most peculiar and implausible way: it is a system built up in minute spaces out of seemingly unsuitable materials (mostly water) and completely devoid of electric wires, radio tubes or the like.

How the human nervous system works is still largely a mystery. But one feature of it is now fairly well understood, and this article will concentrate on that feature. We shall consider how the nerves carry a message—what is commonly known as the "nerve impulse."

The story begins on that September evening in 1786 when Luigi Galvani, professor of anatomy at the University of Bologna, discovered accidentally that a frog's leg touching an iron railing propagated an electric current. The meaning of this observation became a matter of fierce dispute between Galvani and the physicist Alessandro Volta, and not until some sixty years later was it clearly proved that nerve and muscle cells actually possess electrical charge and are capable of generating an electric current. Carlo Matteucci of Pisa and Emil Du Bois-Reymond of Berlin managed to measure and study these tiny electric currents with galvano-meters. But the transient electrical changes that take place at any one point of a nerve fiber are so brief (no more than a few thousandths of a second) that no really precise measurement of them was possible until the development of the modern rapid oscillograph and the cathode-ray tube.

What do we see when we take an electric record of a nerve impulse? The usual procedure is to dissect a frog nerve and place it on two pairs of electrodes. One pair, the "transmitter," is used to stimulate the nerve with an electric pulse; the other pair, the "receiver," is applied at various remote points along the nerve to find out what happens to the velocity and strength of the signal as it travels along. Nowadays we employ an electrostatic cathode-ray tube on which the signal appears as a deflection of some point on a horizontal luminous line which serves as a "time base," so that we get an accurate measurement of the elapsed time of the signal's journey from the transmitting to the receiving point.

We apply a brief electric shock to the nerve from our stimulating electrodes and gradually increase its strength. When it reaches a certain strength, known as the "threshold," we suddenly see an electric wave recorded on the oscilloscope. It arrives after a delay which represents the time the signal has spent in traveling along the nerve from the first to the second pair of electrodes. The signal travels at constant velocity, as we can show by receiving it at various distances from the source. In a frog's motor nerve the speed of travel is about 60 to 100 feet per second; in the fastest fibers of warm-blooded animals the nerve impulse may travel as fast as 300 feet per second.

Now if we strengthen the electrical stimulus, the strength of the signal transmitted by the nerve will also increase—up to a certain maximum. This would suggest that the response of a nerve may vary in degree. But the frog nerve in our experiment is made up of thousands of small nerve fibers, packed tightly together in a bundle. Many years ago some physiologists suggested that the vari-

232

able size of the response might be due simply to variations in the number of fibers brought into play; they argued that an individual fiber probably responded in an "all-or-nothing" fashion—as a match, on being struck, either lights or does not light, depending on whether it has reached the kindling point. Clearly the question could be settled only by investigating the reaction of a single, isolated nerve fiber. Among the first to do this were E. D. Adrian and B. C. Matthews of Cambridge University and D. W. Bronk of Philadelphia, who managed to isolate single fibers under the dissecting microscope. Later it was discovered that some animals, notably the squid, possessed giant nerve fibers which could be studied more easily. And in recent years the physiologist R. W. Gerard and his colleagues at the University of Chicago have developed an ingenious technique for studying the responses of single fibers without going to the trouble of dissecting and isolating them; they use as electrodes submicroscopic micropipettes which can be inserted into a small individual fiber.

What does the experiment on a single fiber show? We insert the tip of a micropipette into the surface of the fiber and find that the fiber interior is electrically charged—some 80 to 90 thousandths of a volt negative with respect to the outside bath. We now apply a brief electric stimulus. Up to a certain strength, there is no response. But as soon as the strength of the stimulus exceeds the "threshold" of our fiber, we observe a large electrical wave. The strength of the response is about 130 thousandths of a volt. Now no matter how much we increase the strength of our stimulus, the size and shape of the electric response is always exactly the same. It is either there in full strength or not there at all. Clearly, then, the propagated impulse in a single fiber is an all-or-none event—a triggered process which is set off like an explosion when the stimulus exceeds the "ignition point" of the fiber.

Thus we have our first solid clue to the nature of the nerve message. It is a standard impulse which in many ways resembles the dot of an elementary communication code. All complicated messages are composed of patterns of the standard dots. To overcome the limitations imposed by this rather rigid and stereotyped system, we have been supplied with a vast number of separate communication channels—many thousands of nerve fibers running side by side in each bundle. The meaning of a composite nerve message depends primarily upon the particular "private lines" that have been selected and upon their peripheral and central connections. Within any single fiber the meaning can be varied only by selecting a suitable pattern of intervals between successive dots.

By a variation of our experiment we can elucidate a second important fact about the nerve impulse. We apply two electric shocks to a nerve fiber in rapid succession. If the second stimulus comes within one or two thousandths of a second after the first, our nerve fiber does not respond: it must have a little rest pause after one impulse to be able to conduct the next. This short period of enforced silence, known as the "refractory period," imposes some interesting limitations upon the practical use to which we may put our nervous communication channels. For example, because of the refractory period a nerve fiber normally can carry only one-way traffic. Any impulses that happened to travel in opposite directions would be stopped and extinguished at the point where they met, for each impulse would have left in its wake a refractory region which could not be traversed by its advancing opposite number. But of course our nervous system is designed to overcome this difficulty; it is supplied with a multitude of channels, so that messages can flow without embarrassment in different directions and to many diverse stations.

The nerve impulse, then, is an electrical signal fired along a nerve fiber. What is the source of electricity? How do we keep the batteries of our cells charged throughout the years of our life? And how exactly does the electric current propagate itself along the whole length of a nerve? During recent years much work has been devoted to these questions in many countries, and we have a good part of the answer.

Some eighty years ago a German physiologist named L. Hermann put forward a remarkable theory. It was known that an electric current could excite nerve tissue and that excited nerve tissue could generate electric current. Putting these two facts together, Hermann suggested that a nerve message travels by steps: a stimulated portion of nerve generates electric current which in turn excites the next portion of nerve which again generates current, and so a wave of electric excitation travels right down to the end of the nerve, much as the process of ignition travels along the length of a fuse by local point-to-point excitation. Hermann's intuitive idea is now known to be correct, and much recent research has been done on the mechanism of the process by which the wave of excitation propagates itself.

A nerve fiber, or axone, is a very long thin tube which grows as a tentacle from a cell body in the brain or spinal cord to make contact with some distant point, such as a muscle or the skin. The fibers vary from less than a 30-thousandth to a thirtieth of an inch in diameter; most human motor and sensory fibers are about a thousandth of an inch thick. In the limbs of large animals the fibers reach a length of several feet. To the electrical engineer this is nothing out of the ordinary; transmission wires or cables are of course many millions of times as long as they are thick. But it is quite a different matter for a microscopic cell body to grow such enormously extended processes and to be responsible for their continued care and maintenance! And there is no doubt that the small cell body, hidden somewhere in the spinal cord, continues to look after the long fiber that belongs to it, for any injury which interrupts the connection to the parent cell causes the whole of the fiber beyond the cut-off point to become inexcitable and die within a few days. Evidently the life of a nerve fiber depends on some physical or chemical principle continually transmitted from the parent cell, but what this is we do not know, and it remains one of our baffling problems.

The key to the electrical activity of a nerve fiber lies in the chemistry of the fiber and of the tissue fluid around it. The nerve tube is filled with a jellylike material, and apparently the degree of "solidity" of this material can be altered by certain substances, in particular calcium ions. Like most jellies, the protoplasm of the nerve fiber owes its solidity to proteins embedded in it. Apart from its jellylike consistency, the physical properties of the fiber material are very similar to those of the outside fluid. Both consist mostly of water with a small quantity of salt dissolved in it, and both are fairly good electrolytic conductors: ions move about at nearly the same speed in both materials. A nerve fiber is usually in osmotic equilibrium with its surroundings; that is, the concentration of dissolved particles inside and outside the fiber is approximately the same. If the salt solution on the outside is diluted a little, water enters the fiber and causes it to swell until a new osmotic equilibrium is re-established.

But in spite of this physical resemblance, the chemical make-up of the fiber interior differs greatly from that of the surrounding fluid. For example, the salt in the surrounding fluid is composed mostly (90 per cent) of sodium and chloride ions, whereas inside the fiber the ions are mainly potassium and various negatively charged organic ions, with sodium and chloride amounting to less than 10 per cent. We are not surprised to find organic ions, for we know that the cell is a chemical factory which can manufacture various organic substances. But how are we to explain the nerve cell's preference for potassium over sodium? Naturally there have been several theories about this, and we are still far from final agreement on the matter. The most obvious thing to suggest is that potassium may have a special chemical affinity to the cell structure and be firmly bound by some of the protein material. This, however, cannot be the correct explanation, because potassium ions must be present as "free agents" inside the cell; otherwise it would be difficult to explain how the interior of the cell can exert its relatively high osmotic pressure or possess its relatively high electric conductivity. The Cambridge physiologists A. L. Hodgkin and

R. D. Keynes have recently proved the mobility of the potassium ions by means of radioactive potassium tracers. A small drop of fluid containing radioactive potassium was placed on a nerve fiber and the tracers were allowed to soak into the fiber. This, by the way, took a very long time, many thousands of times longer than a simple process of diffusion would take. Evidently the ions had to overcome some barrier in moving from the outside solution into the fiber. But once they had penetrated the fiber surface, the tracer ions spread along the inside of the tube with the speed of ordinary free diffusion; that is, they behaved as free, unbound ions. The matter was subjected to a further test by applying an electric potential difference along the axis of the nerve and watching the speed with which the labeled ions moved toward the cathode. The result of this experiment confirmed that the internal potassium ions were free electrical agents and moved without hindrance once they had got inside the cell.

Now there are two main classes of nerve fibers: one kind is enclosed in a "medullary" sheath, and the other lacks such a sheath. This experiment was performed on nonmedullated fibers. These fibers are almost naked, and their surface is freely exposed to the surrounding tissue fluid. Yet the experiment shows that they must have some kind of membrane that acts as a highly resistant barrier to the movement of ions.

This nerve membrane is a fascinating object; it is probably the most delicate and most important part of the nerve cell, and the one most intimately connected with the transmission of signals along the fiber. It has vexed many scientists, however, and some have questioned its existence, because it has not been possible to demonstrate or identify it by direct optical means. It is probably a very thin surface layer made of fatty material only one or two molecules thick—so thin that it would be impossible to examine it even with the most powerful optical instruments. In spite of this disability several of its physical properties have been measured, and most nerve physiologists regard it as just as real, and just as indispensable to an understanding of nerve activity, as are the equally invisible atoms and electrons to understanding the properties of matter.

We know, for instance, that the surface membrane of the nerve fiber is "selectively permeable": it allows some chemical substances to pass much more readily than others. At the beginning of this century the German physiologist S. Bernstein put forward an ingenious explanation of the electrical activity of nerve fibers. He argued that the nerve membrane might be relatively permeable to potassium ions but completely impermeable to sodium, chloride or other ions present in and around the cell. Such a situation would indeed explain how the cell manages to preserve and maintain large differences of concentration and of electric potential across its surface boundary. According to this theory, potassium ions concentrated inside the cell would tend to diffuse out of it, but they are held in by the electrostatic attraction of the organic negative ions, which cannot pass out through the membrane. On the other hand, sodium ions cannot enter to make up for any deficit of positive charges inside the cell. Thus the inside of the cell is more negative (by about one-tenth of a volt) than the surrounding fluid. In a nerve cell at rest the pressure of the potassium ions to get out is balanced by the electrical pressure inward. Bernstein imagined that this balance of forces is a delicately poised affair. Whenever an electric current is passed through a nerve, decreasing the strength of the electric field across the membrane at the cathode, the balance is upset. Bernstein suggested that the excitation is a breakdown of stability of the membrane which might take the form of a sudden increase in its ion permeability. For a moment other ions besides potassium could pass through it relatively freely. As a result the electric field across the fiber membrane would suddenly collapse. Such a temporary "depolarization" of the electrically charged membrane could account for the action potential, or excitation, of the nerve.

The Bernstein theory was bold and ingenious, and for some forty years was accepted by most physiologists as a very satisfactory explanation of the electrical phenomena in nerve fibers. But by 1940 the investigations of research workers began to disturb the theory. The first shock came when E. J. Conway, professor of biochemistry at Dublin, showed that the surface membrane of muscle fibers is certainly permeable to chloride ions, much as to potassium. And when investigators began to test the permeability of the membrane with radioactive tracers, they discovered that it was permeable to sodium ions as well, though less so than to potassium. While the concentration of potassium ions inside the cell and of sodium ions outside remains constant, there is a steady flux of these substances in and out of the cell. All three species of ions—potassium, chloride and sodium—move continually to and fro across the membrane.

The embarrassing question that now confronts us is: How *does* the nerve cell manage to hold down its concentration of sodium ions against the combined forces of diffusion and electrical pressure? We do not yet know. It is generally believed that the resting cell may operate a "sodium pump" which continually drives out sodium ions as fast as they enter. When we speak of a "resting" nerve fiber, all we mean is that the fiber is resting from its usual business of conducting impulses. It is not completely idle; on the contrary it is continually turning over chemical energy and producing heat, even in the absence of signaling activity. No doubt one reason for this continuous turnover is that the cell could not maintain its chemical composition and structure without some expenditure of energy. Fortunately the rate at which sodium ions tend to leak in through the membrane is extremely low, so that the energy required to pump it out is small—well within the working capacity and chemical resources of the resting cell.

Let us stop and sum up what we know about the resting nerve. We have an electrically charged cell, and the source of its electricity appears to be the twofold process which (1) keeps positive sodium ions outside, by pumping them out, and (2) builds up and retains fairly large negative ions inside. In this way a separation of electric charges occurs at the cell surface, the inside being made negative relative to the outside. The potassium and chloride then distribute themselves according to this force: potassium is electrically attracted by the interior of the cell, chloride is rejected, and this goes on until the concentration gradients of these ions balance the electrical force. So long as the cell is capable of pumping out sodium and building up and retaining its organic negative ions, this state of affairs will continue unimpaired.

Now one interesting aspect of this set-up is the fact that the surface membrane offers a very high resistance to the movement of ions in general. We are inevitably reminded of a communication cable. Measurement of the electric conductivity of the various components of a nerve fiber shows that the interior of the fiber behaves like a reasonably good electric conductor, while the membrane has high resistance to direct current (though it allows high-frequency alternating current to pass readily). This set-up bears a rather remarkable resemblance to an electric submarine cable: in both cases we have long cylindrical transmission lines containing an electrically conducting core which is separated from the conducting outside fluid by an insulating sheath. The resemblance, however, is only superficial.

Since the days of Hermann some of the foremost nerve physiologists have considered it worth while to study and analyze the properties of nerve fibers from the point of view of the cable engineer—to find out what the possibilities and deficiencies of a nerve, regarded simply as a passive length of miniature cable, really are. The purpose of a marine cable is to transmit a signal over a very long distance, without fading or loss of clarity. To achieve this a thick insulating sheath is needed, of low capacity and high resistance, so that no leakage of signal strength can occur between the metal core of the cable and the surrounding ocean. It is equally important to provide thick, well-conducting copper strands inside the sheath, so that the electric signal does not lose too much energy as it travels along the core. In all these respects—the dimensions, the gauges and quality of material—our nerve fibers do not seem particularly well endowed for the purpose of long-distance communication. It is true that our nerve signals are not required to travel across the Atlantic Ocean, but a brief subthreshold Morse dot applied to a nerve fiber becomes blurred and indistinguishable after traveling only a tenth of an inch along the fiber, and at a distance of a fifth of an inch from its point of origin the signal has almost completely vanished! Our nerve fibers are very bad cables and could not be used for communication over the long distances in our body, were it not for the fact that they have a booster mechanism which constantly regenerates the signal as it passes along.

The nerve fiber is in effect a chain of relay stations—a device with which the communications engineer is thoroughly familiar. Each point along the fiber receives an electric signal from the preceding point, boosts it to full strength and so enables it to travel a little farther. It is a peculiar combination of a cable (of very defective properties) with an automatic relay mechanism distributed all along the transmission line. Before the electric signal has had a chance to lose its strength it stimulates the fiber, releases local energy resources and is renewed. The electric potential difference across one point of the fiber membrane serves to excite the region ahead, with the result that this region now contributes, at its own expense, a greatly amplified electric signal, capable of spreading to and exciting the next region.

Experiments have fully confirmed this concept of how a nerve fiber transmits a signal. To prove it experimentally one question that must be put to a test is: Does the excitation of a point on the fiber actually generate enough current to excite the next? Direct measurement shows that it does indeed—several times as much as is needed. Hodgkin at Cambridge and R. Lorente de No at the Rockefeller Institute for Medical Research investigated this question in another way; they undertook to find out what it would take to block the passage of the signal. They did this by anesthetizing a stretch of nerve with cold or a drug. Anesthesia makes nerve fiber inexcitable but does not interfere with its ability to conduct a signal cable-fashion. As we have seen, the nerve is a poor cable and the signal quickly loses strength as it travels. The experimenters found that to block a signal they had to anesthetize a sufficiently long stretch of nerve so that the signal lost 90 per cent of its strength before it reached the next excitable point; otherwise it would jump the block. In other words, just a little more than 10 per cent of the current generated by nerve is sufficient to excite normal nerve fiber.

After the proof that the nerve impulse has ample power to regenerate itself from point to point, the next question is: How is the regeneration accomplished? We have already likened nerve excitation to an explosion, and it may be helpful to consider the analogy of the reaction of an explosive gas mixture. Let us take a mixture of hydrogen and oxygen and heat it. If we supply heat at a certain near-threshold rate, here and there a few molecules of hydrogen and oxygen will become excited and react, producing additional heat and raising the temperature further. We have the beginnings of an incipient explosion. But the process is not yet self-sustaining; if we turn off the outside heat supply at this stage, the gas will cool. If we heat the gas to a slightly higher temperature, it may for a little while burn slowly by itself (without outside heat) at a rate which exactly balances the loss of heat to the cooler surroundings. At this point a very minute addition of heat will cause the whole gas to explode and burn itself out.

Now a similar, but reversible, process occurs when we apply a pulse of current to a nerve membrane. The current tends to reduce the electric potential across the membrane. Up to a certain strength of applied current, the nerve recovers its original potential as soon as the pulse of current ends. But just below the threshold of excita-

Action potential wave (*top*) spreads along the surface of a nerve fiber (*bottom*). During the rise of the action potential, sodium ions (Na) enter the fiber and make it positive; during the resting state of the nerve the outward pressure of potassium ions (K) keeps fiber interior negative.

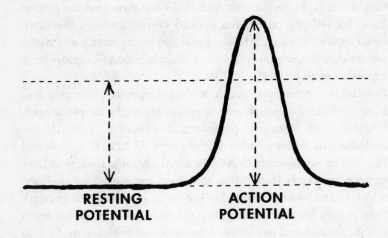

RESTING POTENTIAL   **ACTION POTENTIAL**

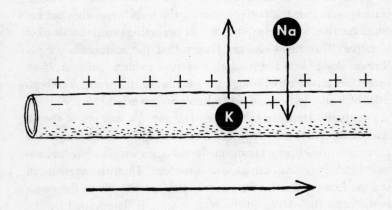

tion of the nerve, we see signs of a partial reaction, like the beginning of an explosive process. And above the threshold the process becomes self-generating: the applied current reduces the membrane potential; this starts some reaction in the membrane which reduces the potential further, and the chain proceeds rapidly in an explosive manner.

What is this reaction, and how does it operate? Bernstein had suggested that the electric nerve impulse makes the membrane permeable to ions other than potassium, as a result of which the potential across the membrane drops to zero. In 1938 K. S. Cole and H. J. Curtis at Columbia University and the Marine Biological Laboratory in Woods Hole, Mass., obtained some exciting evidence which at first seemed to provide enormous support for Bernstein's theory: they found that the passage of an impulse through a nerve membrane reduced its electrical resistance 40-fold, i.e., made it 40 times more permeable to the passage of ions. But within a year Hodgkin and A. F. Huxley at Cambridge discovered a disconcerting fact: that the potential across the membrane does not become zero but is reversed, the interior becoming positive instead of negative. This ruled out the theory that the membrane simply "breaks down" and becomes equally permeable to all ions. If all ions could pass freely through the membrane, the charges on both sides of it should become neutralized, not reversed.

Eventually Hodgkin and Huxley suggested a way out of the dilemma. Suppose, they proposed, that during the excitation of the nerve the membrane momentarily becomes much more permeable to sodium ions than to any other ions. Then the pressure of sodium ions rushing into the nerve interior will reverse the membrane potential, which in the resting state is determined by the potassium pressure from the inside out.

This modern "sodium theory" assumes that the sodium permeability of the nerve membrane is a delicately balanced affair and depends upon the electric field to which the membrane material is subjected. When a current passes through the membrane, partially discharging the membrane surface and thus reducing the electric field, this makes the membrane more permeable to sodium. Positive sodium ions begin to flow inward and further reduce the negative charge on the inside. Thus the electric field across the membrane is further reduced, the sodium permeability continues to rise, more sodium enters, and we have the elements of a self-reinforcing chain reaction. The flow of sodium into the fiber continues until the fiber interior has been charged up to such a high positive level that sodium ions are electrostatically repelled. This new equilibrium is precisely the reverse of the resting potassium potential. Now we can understand the basis of the all-or-none reaction of nerve cells: they generate no current until the "ignition point" is approached. Once this point is passed, the production of "sodium current" proceeds toward saturation and runs through a cycle of its own no longer under the control of the original stimulus.

It would take too long to describe all the experiments that have been carried out to test the "sodium story." For one thing, it has been proved that many types of nerve fibers require sodium in the tissue fluid to conduct impulses. Secondly, the height of the action potential can be varied over a wide range by altering the amount of sodium on the outside of the membrane, and quantitatively it follows the predictions of the theory. Third, measurements of the passage of sodium into the fiber interior during a series of impulses have shown that it is sufficient in quantity to account for the strength of the action current. Finally, in an ingenious series of experiments Hodgkin and Huxley have been able to measure the rate of sodium transfer across a cylinder of nerve membrane, when the electric field as well as the external sodium concentration was varied over a wide and carefully controlled range. A number of interesting facts emerged. When the electric field was suddenly reduced from the normal resting level to zero, a sudden rush of sodium ions occurred down their concentration gradient; normally they flowed into the fiber, but when the outside concentration had been reduced to a level below that inside the fiber, the flux of sodium was reversed! It seems clear, therefore, that the critical change during electric stimulation is indeed an increase of permeability to sodium ions—permeability in either direction. Another important fact which emerged is that the sudden flow of sodium ions is only a transient change: after one or two thousandths of a second it is automatically "switched off" again and converted into an increased flow of potassium ions! Why this is so remains mysterious, but it certainly serves an extremely useful purpose. The accelerated outflow of potassium allows the membrane potential to return rapidly to the original resting level, so that the nerve can repeat the firing of its brief, sharp electric signal almost immediately.

We do not yet know why the permeability of the membrane to sodium varies with the electric field. It is quite probable that sodium moves across the membrane in several steps, not as free ions but perhaps attached to molecules within the fatty material of the membrane. In other words, a sodium ion may first combine with a negatively-charged "carrier molecule," which acts as a guide through the membrane, and then may jump off as a free ion again into the water on the inner surface. According to this theory, which is still only speculative, the negative carrier molecules may be held immobilized to the positive outer membrane surface when the electric field is large, and may become mobile when the electric field is reduced.

It hardly needs to be said that nerve physiologists do not all agree on these new ideas concerning the mechanism of the nerve impulse. Some distinguished experimenters prefer the idea that sodium and potassium act merely as "lubricants," rather than as direct carriers, of the transfer of charge across the fiber membrane. Others consider it possible that the charge may be transported across the membrane by hydrogen ions, or even by electrons, rather than by sodium and potassium ions. No doubt these issues will remain controversial for years to come.

There is, however, complete agreement on one matter: namely, that nerve signals are propagated step by step along the fiber by some electrochemical relay mechanism. In the case of nonmedullated fibers the signal is relayed from point to adjacent point. The type of fiber that is enclosed in a thick medullary sheath operates its signal service in an even more interesting fashion. It has its relay stations distributed at relatively few points, namely at gaps in the medullary sheath, known as the "nodes of Ranvier." These points are spaced rather regularly along the fiber at intervals of one or a few millimeters. The sheathed sections between these points form a relatively good passive cable, as biological materials go. The development of a medullary sheath occurred at a relatively advanced stage of evolution and brought with it a great increase in the speed and economy of nerve-signal traffic. A medullated nerve fiber passes messages some ten times as quickly, and with about a tenth of the expenditure of energy, as a nonmedullated fiber of the same diameter. By providing an insulating, low-capacity sleeve, it restricts the expensive and time-consuming process of relaying to a few points along the line.

It is interesting to speculate on the alternative means that evolution might have chosen to speed up the rate of signaling in our nerve fibers. There could really have been only one alternative: to increase the diameter of the fibers. But its disadvantages are obvious. We need an enormous number of parallel private lines to pass the large number of vital messages between our brain center and the innumerable points on the periphery of the body. The eye alone has one million private telephone lines in the optic nerve. Without a medullary sheath, their diameter would have to be increased some 50-fold to retain their speed; but at 50 times their present size there would not be enough room in our head to accommodate this vast number of communication channels. It is fortunate indeed that nature managed to invent the segmented medullary sheath for us!

THE ELECTRICAL ACTIVITY
OF THE BRAIN

by W. Grey Walter

TWENTY-FIVE YEARS AGO Hans Berger, a German psychiatrist working in Jena, began to publish some strange little pictures consisting of nothing but wavy lines. They should have caused great excitement among his colleagues, because he claimed that they showed the electrical activity of a human brain. But in fact no one took them seriously. For several years no one even bothered to repeat his experiments.

Berger was naturally hurt and disappointed that his epoch-making discovery was ignored or ridiculed. But there were three understandable reasons why any well-trained scientist should have dismissed Berger's claims. First, it was not considered really respectable to study the activity of the brain with measuring tools. Classical scientific methods depend on measuring one thing at a time as exactly as possible, and it was plainly impossible to isolate the individual functions of the complex human brain. Second, the "brain waves" Berger published were altogether dull—merely a tiny electrical oscillation at about 10 waves per second. It was inconceivable that these simple, regular lines could disclose anything significant about so mysterious an organ as the human brain. Third, Berger had rather unwisely admitted that he was looking for what he claimed to have found; psychiatrists, rightly or wrongly, have a reputation for being able to find proof of their wildest ideas when it suits their beliefs.

This little episode in the history of brain research should be a lesson to everyone with a brain to study, for it shows that curiosity and imagination are too easily stifled by the usual scientific training, emphasizing self-criticism and technical skill. Berger was in fact a modest and careful observer; his misfortune was that his technique did not equal his enthusiasm. In the quarter-century since then the study of his little wavy lines has grown into a new department of science called electroencephalography. Today several hundred laboratories in the U. S. and a similar number in Europe are recording and interpreting charts of the electrical discharges of human brains. Their total annual output of charts would girdle the earth. Hospitals all over the world have accumulated thousands upon thousands of brainprints of their patients, for these recordings have proved to be a great help in the diagnosis and treatment of brain diseases.

Brain diseases leave prints as distinctive as a criminal's fingerprints, and the brainprints have been useful in medical practice for precisely the same purpose—to identify the culprit. Just as a fingerprint serves this purpose although its details reveal nothing about the criminal's character, so a brainprint may be put to use for identifying a brain disorder even though we do not understand what it may have to tell about what is going on in the brain. The detective work involved in tracking down the clues to brain diseases is so exciting that at first scientists were content to exploit this aspect of electroencephalography and to postpone more fundamental investigations. During the last few years, however, interest has been swinging round to use of the tool to study the working of the living brain itself.

By a fortunate coincidence—or perhaps it is not a coincidence—the designers of the new electronic computers have, at the same time, become more and more impressed with the similarities between their machines and the mechanisms of the brain. Physiologists have had the satisfaction of seeing engineers develop, with great labor and expense, systems which evolved naturally in living creatures millions of years ago. This convergence of interest—the cross-fertilization between communication engineering and biology—has been given the name cybernetics, originally used by the

French physicist André Marie Ampère over a hundred years ago. Norbert Wiener, professor of mathematics at the Massachusetts Institute of Technology, focused interest on the subject with his book in 1949, and it has since been pursued at several conferences convened by the Josiah Macy Jr. Foundation. Through these discussions runs a thread of longing and conjecture—if only we could unravel by our physical methods the mystery of how the brain functions!

The machines that record the electrical rhythms in the brain have become elaborate and expensive. They contain dozens or even hundreds of radio tubes. A really elaborate research apparatus may have several hundred controls, set and adjusted by a team of highly skilled operators before and during each experiment. The cost of the equipment is usually defrayed by the fees earned in medical applications; the gigantic scale of this work could never have been achieved with the funds available for academic research. The astonishing thing is that with all this time and material we still do not understand even one part in a thousand of the frantic scribblings of our fine machines.

The standard electroencephalographic chart shows a set of eight or more wavy lines, each line being a graph of the electric signals from one region of the head. We may suppose—and it is only a supposition—that these signals are coded messages from the brain, and our task may be defined as a search for clues that will help us to break the cipher and read the messages. The usefulness of the brainprints in diagnosing disease lies in the fact that we have established that serious emergencies in the brain usually yield certain simple code messages in our machines.

The signals are usually classified by the frequency of the electrical pulsations in them. Berger's original oscillations, which he named *alpha* rhythms, are in the frequency band between 8 and 13 cycles per second—that is, about as fast as you can move a finger. Their size, or amplitude, is around 30 millionths of a volt. Neither the frequency nor the amplitude is constant. Each individual has his own characteristic pattern of shifts in frequency and size; thus his brainprint is as distinctive as his signature. The alpha rhythms also can be identified by the part of the brain they come from; they are nearly always largest at the back of the head, where the nerve signals from the eyes reach the brain. They are usually larger and more regular when a person has his eyes shut and is not thinking. From this the inference has been drawn that activity of the visual imagination may suppress the alpha rhythms. One person in five shows no alpha rhythm at all—only small, complex, irregular pulsations from all parts of the brain, with no fixed frequency. In one in five also the alpha rhythms go on even when the eyes are open. Upon the basis of such personal differences we have established a tentative classification of brain types in human beings. This system indicates differences in ways of thinking, rather than the relative success of people's thinking, as "intelligence tests" do.

Let it be said at once that nobody has yet been able to determine precisely the meaning of the alpha and other electrical rhythms of the brain. Nonetheless they are much too prominent, too individual, too persistent—and already too clearly related to mental activities—to be dismissed as "disappointingly constant," as they were when the brain physiologist E. D. Adrian demonstrated them at Cambridge University in 1934.

Some time ago I was struck by a peculiar coincidence. I had reflected a thousand times that the brain rhythms are a unique phenomenon: Nowhere else in nature are such intricate patterns to be found, such variety, such interweaving of differential frequencies in their ever-changing combinations and permutations. On the thousand and first reflection I followed up this thought with the question: What is the unique function of the brain? The brain's unique function is to learn. The conclusion from this seemed inescapable: probably there is some kind of coupling between learning and the brain's unique physical activity—its electrical rhythms.

Since then we have gone some way toward verifying the learning theory, as will be told later in this chapter. But the immediate problem that presents itself to the thoughtful reader will be: What is the physiological function of the electrical rhythms? Apart from such end results as learning, what are the rhythms for, what do they do, what is their special role in brain mechanisms?

Let us concentrate on the alpha rhythms, definitely known to be associated with vision. One of the great physiological puzzles about vision is this: When an image is received by the brain, how is it passed on to the cognition areas? We know that a scene registered on the retina in the eye is projected on a section of the brain cortex by the optic nerve—a compact bundle of a million or so nerve fibers. From the visual projective cortex, information about the things seen is somehow transferred to billions of other cells in the brain. Can we imagine that the million points of projection are connected with all those billions of cells? It is quite inconceivable that anything like the necessary number of physical links could be housed in the head. We are therefore led to the suggestion, derived from the examples of radar and television, that communication between the projection and the cognition areas must be by a scanning mechanism.

This suggestion gains force when we consider what may have been the evolutionary origin of brain rhythms. Such a rhythm means that a group of millions of brain cells are firing together at regular intervals. The most primitive living example of cellular collaboration of this kind is the jellyfish. We may suppose that an early form of jellyfish depended for its existence upon the food signals received by its nerve net, which produced a convulsion (comparable to an epileptic seizure) that propelled the animal toward the exciting food. Such an action implies a combined discharge of many motor cells. The nerve net presumably consisted of specialized food-and-motor cells and steering cells. A cell receiving the food stimulus would pass it to the steering cells and these would transmit it to the other motor cells almost—but not quite—simultaneously. In other words, besides the time lag always required for recharging the cells, there would be a time lag in the communication of the signal to all the cells. There is already here something suggestive of scanning; the whole of the forward nerve net would be open to suggestion and the impulse would be propagated by whichever cell first received the incentive.

Further evolutionary specialization might produce a system in which the signal or incentive was passed from the perceptive cells to the steering cells and from there to the motor cells, the steering cells thus assuming a primitive brain function. This is where one would have to look for a rhythmic discharge like that of the alpha rhythms. It has been suggested that the alpha rhythms may be a necessary periodical wiping out of the impressions received on the visual projection cortex. Such a process may seem plausible in a primitive perceptive-steering-motor system, but it would not account for the phenomena of the human brain. Moreover, for a primitive system such as the one described it would not be necessary. The discharge of the steering cells as they communicated their impulse to the motor cells would itself wipe out the previous impression and allow them to present a clear field for the next impulse. But again to carry the matter a step further in brain evolution, the time lag in transmission of the signals would establish an inherent rhythmic sympathy among all the steering cells, geared to the period of the passing of signals from the perception cells. Putting it very crudely, this is in effect what seems to be taking place in the human brain: the alpha waves sweep to and fro scanning the visual cortex in harmony with the period during which a scene is retained by the transmitting retina.

As already mentioned, the diversity of alpha rhythms is their most intriguing property. What, however, are we to say about the many people who display little or no alpha rhythm? According to the scanning hypothesis, their scanner must be working at very low amplitude, yet these are the people in whom visual imagery is most vivid and persistent. At first this seemed a crude paradox, but we were blinded by the vision of familiar machines. In a TV set, scanning of the field goes on continually whatever the picture may be; in certain radar sets designed to control artillery and in many target-seeking projectiles, a scanner is set to search for targets, but once an echo has been received the scanner stops and swings the gun or missile into a position of best attack. This simple system was incorporated into the toy robot, *Machina speculatrix*, which we made years ago to see how "scanning" would affect behavior. In systems such as these, the more active and excited the system is, the less regular and rhythmic the scanning cycle becomes. So perhaps within our heads we carry a bundle of target-seeking tissue—in origin primeval, but in function as penetrating and as precise as any imagined, even in the realms of science fiction. Here we can discern at work the organ of selection and imagination, first stages on the road to learning, understanding and foreseeing the shifting patterns of the outside world—and all contained in a cupful of tepid, pinkish-gray, electric jelly.

To complete the panorama of the strange dark world within our heads, let us look at the brainprint itself. Learning to understand brainprints is rather like learning a foreign language from a number of acquaintances with different accents and dialects. Now there are two things which often astonish a visitor to a foreign land: (1) the ease with which young children speak the tongue, and (2) the similarity of baby talk in all countries. We are called mammals because "ma" is one of the first syllables human babies everywhere fix upon, and they seem to apply it to the maternal organ which first regularly attracts their attention. There are similar characters in brainprints. At birth the brainprints of infants are generalized, but at an early age, around three or four, the child's brainprint acquires the individualistic features of an adult's. In a newborn babe there are slow, rhythmic swings of electric change in all areas of the brain, the different parts acting in the same way electrically but without much co-ordination. During sleep the brainprints of babies are very like those of sleeping

254

adults: mainly large, slow, regular oscillations, called *delta* rhythms. Some time during the first few months of life an important mechanism appears—a transient outburst of fast and slow rhythms when the sleeping baby is half awakened by a noise or movement. Most parents are only too familiar with the transition from an infant who will sleep through almost any racket to one which stirs at the creak of a floor board. The same electrical response to stimuli when asleep is seen in adults. In most cases it seems to be connected with the brain mechanism that prevents a sleeper from being awakened too easily by trivial noises; it has been called the "K" complex. In later life these safety mechanisms are usually very sharply tuned, as it were, so that a mother may sleep through a thunderstorm but wake when her baby whimpers.

During the first few years of life the slow rhythms get steadily smaller as the nerve fibers in the brain complete their growth. At about the end of the first year another sort of rhythm appears. It has a frequency of five or six per second and is largest at the sides of the head. It seems to be connected in some way with what we call emotion, particularly with feelings of annoyance and frustration. In children of about three years old it can be evoked very easily by teasing—by offering a piece of candy and then snatching it away again. Another similar rhythm can easily be evoked by simple physical pleasure. These rhythms have been called *theta* rhythms, because they seem to be connected in some way with the functioning of the thalamus, the midbrain where signals from the body are relayed to the brain roof. The theta rhythms usually appear at that phase of development when children start to acquire self-control. The age at which this happens varies, and so do the size and character of the theta rhythms.

The first sign of alpha rhythms is seen clearly during the second or third year, but the faster components rarely appear until the age of seven or eight. The theta rhythms and alpha rhythms are present together in varying proportions until the age of thirteen or fourteen. Consequently the interpretation of children's brainprints is particularly difficult, demanding appreciation of psychological and social factors influencing the individual child. For instance, adults usually submit to electroencephalography calmly, but for children the mere fact of being in a hospital, of not being allowed to sit on mother's knee, of having to keep still and so forth, has a startling effect on the brain activity. It is often possible to tell a good deal about a child's fears and interests from the way in which the brain rhythms change during a recording or from one examination to another. His brainprint may even vary according to whether the operator is wearing a white or a green coat.

An adult whose brain becomes diseased or injured, or who has a childish personality, may revert to the slow delta and theta rhythms of infancy and childhood. In certain conditions of strain unusually fast rhythms appear. In certain types of epilepsy there is a characteristic combination of enormous slow waves and fast spikes. Naturally the exact location of these abnormal features is a very important part of electroencephalography, for it can pinpoint a disturbance for an operation by a brain surgeon.

This catalogue of the signals received from the living brain may give a misleading impression of simplicity. Only in very severe or advanced stages of a brain disease are the brainprints so clear that their features can be designated with complete confidence. Far more often all these slow and fast components appear together intermittently or continuously in various parts of the brain, all of them varying with the state of the person being studied. The record is usually more like the score of a symphony or the transcript of conversations at a cocktail party than a simple code message. Whenever it takes on the character of a solo or a monologue, one knows that something has gone seriously wrong, either with the brain or with the recording machine.

Using again the analogy with cipher breaking, the difficulty with electroencephalography is not to pick up a message but that inevitably a great many different messages are received at the same time. This situation has demanded several refinements of technique. The human eye is ill adapted to sorting out the components of a complex curve. Sometimes different rhythms combine in such a way as to give a completely false impression. For example, during an examination in which a person becomes annoyed by something, the curve may change in a way which seems to indicate that the frequency of his alpha rhythm has dropped by one or two cycles per second. Actually the true change may be the breaking out of an entirely separate theta rhythm which is imposed on the alpha.

To unravel the situation many laboratories now employ special wave analyzers. These instruments deal with the complex electrical oscillations from the brain in rather the same way as a prism separates the colors in a beam of light. The components of the complex wave are isolated by electronic circuits tuned to the several frequencies. A moving pen automatically records the amount of activity at each frequency during a fixed interval, usually ten seconds. The result is a set of curves giving the frequency spectrum of the brainprint. This process is repeated over and over, and other electronic circuits write out the statistical average of the spectrum readings every minute or so, so that the experimenter can measure not only the composition of the brain signals from time to time but also their variability over a longer period. From this can be assessed the versatility of the brain under investigation —an important measure of its repertoire of adaptive stratagems.

Frequency analysis by this means has proved a valuable tool, but like all tools it has its limitations. It cannot easily be applied to more than one part of the brain at once. Few laboratories can afford more than two analyzers, for they cost upward of $5,000 apiece. Furthermore, frequency analysis can be quite misleading unless it is used imaginatively; it can only suggest possible solutions to a problem, and the experimenter must then make further studies to decide which of the possible solutions is correct. Since the state of the brain is always changing, the fresh tactics suggested by frequency analysis may come too late to be of immediate value. Again, using the cipher comparison, frequency analysis will not give information about how the rapidly changing signals from different parts of the brain are related to one another, or which of the suggested meanings is the most likely one.

Yet the sort of insight that frequency analysis is capable of providing is vividly illustrated by a recent laboratory experience. The investigator had just taken delivery of a new analyzer and had spent a Saturday morning tuning and calibrating his new treasure. By afternoon he was ready to try it, but the only test subject left in the laboratory was a technical assistant who had, by ordinary standards, rather a dull record. (Electroencephalographers mean no offense when they call a record "dull"—in fact, the best companions often give the dullest records. The reference is only to the lack of larger regular oscillations.) On this Saturday afternoon an international football match happened to be going on, and the subject listened to the radio while the test proceeded. After a few minutes the experimenter, who was not listening to the radio but was busily adjusting the settings of his new instrument and checking the consistency of its analysis, began to realize that he was unconsciously following the progress of the football game as it affected his subject. At first, when the home side was in the lead and the play was relatively uninteresting, the subject's alpha rhythm droned on at nine cycles per second, and there was only a trace of theta activity. Then the game livened up; the analyzer promptly showed an alpha rise to ten cycles per second. When the visiting team scored a goal, the theta rhythms suddenly increased to the size of the alpha rhythms. This complex spectrum of theta and rapid alpha activity persisted with only minor fluctuations until the game ended with the defeat of the home team. One may say that, knowing the score, one could tell the nationality of the subject from his brainprint, or knowing the subject, one could infer the state of the game. Testing a roomful of people, the instrument could show which of them were interested in football and whether an individual's interest was mainly in the niceties of play or in which side won.

Prolonged and detailed analysis of records from normal subjects has shown that the spectrum of alpha rhythms is far more complex than was at first supposed. When a person is performing a task—e.g., trying to recognize an object by its feel—the various components in the alpha band wax and wane in a manner absolutely characteristic of that person. One component may be linked with the attempt to visualize what has been felt, another with a search for verbal expression, another with the recall of visual impressions, another with the effort to imagine a color, and so forth. For each person there are typical combinations and permutations of rhythmic change, associated with the way that person prefers to solve problems and handle the model of the world his head contains.

To watch the unfolding brainprints of a friend is an absorbing experience, particularly if you have some idea of his state of mind and interests of the moment. You have the impression, however, of listening to a muttered soliloquy through a keyhole. You itch to ask a leading question, but only rarely can you frame a question simple enough to evoke an intelligible change in the brainprint. In 1945 there was introduced a method of stimulation, simpler than ordinary language, which has vastly extended the scope of electroencephalography. It is based on a principle well known to cryptographers. If you are trying to break a code, a useful trick is to force the enemy to send a message of your own selection: e.g., "100 bombers approaching." When you pick up this known message in his code, you have the key in your hand. Radar, which obtains information from a reflected radio pulse of predetermined frequency, is another aspect of much the same principle. The idea was applied to the study of the brain by stimulating the eyes with very short flashes of light at controlled intervals.

The way this method developed is an interesting example of

interplay between clinical needs and scientific conjecture. When frequency analysis was first applied to brainprints from epileptics, it was discovered that in many the rhythms had a tendency to appear in distinct bands with an almost arithmetical relationship to one another. For example, there might be activity at the frequencies of 3, 6, 9 and 24 cycles per second. During an epileptic fit these highly distinctive patterns became pronounced. This suggested that a seizure might be induced by electrical stimulation which accentuated the "harmonic" relation between these rhythms in different parts of the brain, or which synchronized the rhythms and supplied missing links in the harmonic series—12, 15, 18 or 21 in the example given. This sounds cruel, but the diagnosis of epilepsy is never sure until an attack has been seen by an experienced observer, and all kinds of disagreeable methods have been suggested for inducing an attack in unfortunate people who may be epileptic. The flicker method of synchronizing the inherent brain rhythms seemed to be relatively gentle and promised to be scientifically illuminating. Almost the first time the method was tried on a known epileptic, a dramatic success was achieved; the moment a certain combination of light flashes was established, the patient underwent one of his characteristic attacks. The success of this clinical stratagem naturally encouraged more detailed study of the way normal brains responded to flickering lights, and it was soon found that in most people stimulation of this sort evoked in the brain extraordinarily complicated and widespread responses.

Among other discoveries, it was found possible to make the brain stimulate itself by positive feedback. The electric impulses from the brain were connected through the recording machine to the electronic gadget that produced the flashes of light. In this way a brain response to a flash triggered a new flash and so on. This method of self-excitement is particularly effective for revealing a hidden tendency to epileptic seizures. It resembles very closely the way an engineer may test the stability of a transmission system: he applies positive feedback to disturb the system and observes how effectively the system's inherent negative feed-back operates to damp the disturbance and restore equilibrium. A normal brain contains an automatic gain control which prevents overexcitement even during positive-feedback flicker experiments.

The importance of these discoveries is that they demonstrate the dynamic and personal response of the brain to a stimulus. When it receives a light signal, it sends a coded message to nearly every part of the brain. Usually messages arriving in brain regions far from the visual receiving department evoke no action; they are "to whom it may concern, for information only." But the administrative rules, so to say, are not watertight; the signaling procedure has certain weaknesses. In many epileptics and even in one normal person in twenty, the relayed message is acted upon immediately by the executive part of the brain and something like an epileptic fit results. It is as though all the officials in a government office were to reply in exhaustive detail to instructions intended only for a single department. The reason flicker stimuli are so potent seems to be that they overwhelm the brain's channels of communication with their barrage of rapid, repetitive impulses. You cannot drive a nail into a piece of wood with your finger however hard you push, but the same amount of energy applied in repeated hammer blows will do the trick.

An encouraging feature of the flicker stimulation method is that anyone looking at the flickering light sees more than just flicker. There is always a sensation of movement, pattern and color, though the stimulus is stationary, featureless and without distinctive hue. Margiad Evans, a novelist who underwent this experience, described her sensations as follows:

"Lights like comets dangled before me, slow at first and then gaining a furious speed and change, whirling color into color, angle into angle. They were all pure, ultra-unearthly colors, mental colors, not deep visual ones. There was no glow in them, but only activity and revolution."

Red flickers are more effective than those of any other color.

Some people develop exaggerated electrical responses and sensations only with red flicker. Conversely, it has been found that some epileptics have fewer spontaneous fits when they wear spectacles that screen out the red wavelengths of light.

The cause of these visual illusions during flicker has intrigued us considerably. The intricate moving patterns may be subjective evidence for the scanning process outlined above; we have found that brief, intermittent stationary signals applied to a space-time converter or scanner will always produce an illusion of pattern or movement, just as such signals applied to a moving system can provide an illusion that the system is stationary—the stroboscopic effect. A person contemplating the illusions of "activity and revolution" is, in effect, examining the sweep of his own brain, raking and sifting the clutter of signals for anything which may have meaning or value.

From the experimental standpoint the outstanding virtue of the flicker method is that the stimulus is "tagged" with the frequency at which the light is flashing, so that frequency analysis can be used to particular advantage. Brainprints contain a great deal of confusing information—activity unconnected with the particular experiment. These interfering signals cannot be eliminated, because they are an essential part of brain functions—the sign of continuous active adaptation in the organ of adaptation. In searching for the response to an experimental stimulus against this background we are rather in the position of someone who has an appointment to meet a strange lady at a busy terminus: how to pick her out of the throng of passersby? The usual solution is to arrange to wear a flower of a certain color and wait at a certain place at a certain time. The combination of flicker and frequency analysis has the same effect. The stimulus has a known frequency and the amount of spontaneous activity at that frequency in the various parts of the brain can easily be measured beforehand. Any increase in the activity at that frequency during the stimulation period can be seen quite clearly in the analysis, even when it is completely hidden in the busy crowd of other rhythms and discharges. A regular response only one-millionth of a volt in size can be measured even when the interfering signals are twenty times as big. Viewed in this way, the strange, remote responses to flicker are rather as though, having arranged to recognize a blind date by her red carnation, one came upon all her uncles and aunts in every corner of the rendezvous, wearing flowers of similar shades and with mysterious assignations.

Meeting under the clock has romantic associations, but the comparison with frequency analysis is not quite accurate; though we can recognize very small rhythmic signals by their frequency, the time and place of their occurrence are indeterminate. The ordinary written record could supply this information, but to interpret the multiple responses in detail is like listening to half a dozen witnesses all giving their testimony at once and chattering to one another as well. We wanted something that would give evidence in a curt, formal way, would be content to answer "yes" or "no" to leading questions, and would indicate when there was general agreement about the responses in different parts of the brain. We dreamed of developing a combination of expert witness, learned counsel and impartial jury.

In 1947 we began to work out an entirely new method of displaying brain signals which we hoped would enable us to eliminate the interference from irrelevant signals—to cloak with invisibility the crowd of strangers milling around our dear unknown. The machine that has "just growed" in our laboratory is called the Toposcope—Topsy for short—because it was originally intended to show the topography (space pattern) of the brain activity. Like the Taj Mahal, which it faintly resembles, the conception has grown in scope by marriage to four other instruments (each with its technical and pet name) so that it is now much more than merely an indicator of the topography.

In principle Topsy is rather like twenty-two small television or radar sets. Twenty-two little cathode-ray tubes, each connected by an electrode to a different region of the subject's head, translate into visual form, as pictures of changing brightness, the activity of the respective parts of the brain; they bring the brain signals, amplified, to their screens. When no signals are present, there is nothing to see; but when the brain is active, the tubes light up, and the display becomes "an enchanted loom where flashing shuttles weave a dissolving pattern: always a meaningful pattern but never an abiding one." Sir Charles Sherrington's poetic image describes exactly the impression these scopes give. An automatic camera records snapshots of these scenes, transforming into frozen vectors the procession of illuminated butterflies which recalls the passionate Psyche of the classic Mind.

The display tubes are arranged behind a plastic screen mapping the head as seen from above. Each tube is a sort of clock face too, for in each the electron beam which the brain signals turn on and off is formed by special circuits into a rotating line or spoke, like the sweep hand of a radar receiver. All these electronic clock hands turn at the same speed, and the speed is controlled either by the experimenter or by the subject's brain itself. When the operator controls the speed, the time scale is ordinary clock time; when the subject's brain controls it, the time is "local" time—the time scale of that part of the brain at that moment. The varying relation between brain time and standard time shows as a blurring of the needle on a meter which records the time of each revolution of the hand. Thus parts of the brain that keep the same time can be picked out quite easily, and the signals they exchange can be distinguished from the gossip and backchat of bystanders and the welter of routine traffic. Since the instrument can also deliver stimuli in various patterns at selected times, the marriages of new sensations to pre-existing activity can be watched as an electric concordance of great variety and beauty.

When we began to use this machine, we found the time maps hard to understand. But gradually the new code has begun to penetrate our thick heads, and much of what was quite bewildering in the ordinary brainprints now seems to be taking on a new form and luster. When the brain is receiving a time pattern of visual signals (for example, a series, or group, of flashes, then an interval, then another group and so on), the pattern often is "dissected"; adjacent areas respond to selected parts of the pattern in sequence, as if some scanning process is "turning on" one part of the brain after another. In areas distant from the visual region, the responses are recombined in an arrangement resembling the original pattern.

These two effects—dissection and remote resynthesis—seem to solve partly two of the main mysteries posed by the brainprints, namely, the function of the alpha rhythms and the widespread effects of flicker stimulation. In most normal subjects activity appears in the temporal or the frontal lobes, which are remote from the visual projective area, mainly when the visual pattern is novel or interesting. There the pattern may be complete again, sometimes simplified or even abstracted, as it were, shorn of irrelevant variations and inconsistencies. In the temporal lobes, when the stimulation ceases the pattern hangs on—a phantom of meaning which as the seconds pass dwindles into the nothingness of all forgotten things. In subjects too experienced in these trials no hint of these strange processes is seen. The processes are not the well-worn trade routes of automatic life; rather they are the speculative, adventurous machinery that guides the living brain to matching within itself the indifferent or hostile change and chance of the world it must manipulate.

Here we confront the great problem of how the brain can decide that an association or coincidence of events is not mere chance. Breaking the problem down, it can be shown that for even the most rudimentary learning by association seven distinct operations must be performed to decide whether one series of events implies another. To illustrate this hypothesis, three years ago, we designed the seven-step sequence into a simple electronic learning circuit to which we gave the name *Machina docilis*. By building and observing such models, we may hope to explain or at least to describe somewhat more coherently the features of brain function which the Toposcope is beginning to illuminate. *M. docilis* can learn only one simple lesson. In the human brain no bounds can yet be set for learning, but on the lowest level we are beginning to have some confidence that the mechanisms of understanding are not unimaginably beyond our understanding.

The pictures of brain response produced by the Toposcope indicate that, as required by theory, signals entering the brain are subjected to considerable processing before they reach the primary receiving areas. Somewhere in the middle of the head is a diffuse foliage of nerve cells and tendrils that picks up from the stream of incoming messages a series of hints that "something has happened." This information, crude, unspecific but emphatic, is broadcast to many distant regions. The effect is to alert the whole brain. When the situation is novel and the intensity of the signals high, the widespread responses are almost in the nature of an alarm—"anything may happen." But, as we have seen, familiarity breeds indifference; the brain learns to assess the message and to file it away unless in fact it turns out to signal some important event. In the course of time, after many trials and rehearsals, the brain establishes the meaning and importance of new messages.

Our electronic model for this operation, *M. docilis*, suggests that this assessment of importance can be accurate only if the brain operates as a statistical computer. We conjecture that the living brains we are examining with our recording machine are engaged in working out as best they can the chances that what we are doing may have some meaning—some relevance to the problem of their survival. When, in moments of relatively lucid experimentation, we hit upon a message which apparently does convey some meaning, then the texture of the electric fabric woven before our eyes acquires indeed a meaningful pattern. In those of our subjects who suffer from seizures or disorders of consciousness during flicker, the "pari-mutuel" within the brain jumps the lines and

266

throws out a wild and vulgar guess, as though everything meant anything. This conclusion is so utterly inconsistent with the continuation of life that only a general shutdown can avert catastrophe, and the patient lapses into a daze.

The application of these methods and theories to clinical problems is becoming a serious preoccupation. Mental or nervous disorders which are undetectable in conventional brainprints often show up markedly when studied with the Toposcope during stimulation or excitement. One significant clue is the length of persistence of an electrical pattern after the stimulus is terminated. In some people whose thinking is confused and incoherent this "memory" time seems to be ten times as long as in ordinary folk. When a succession of different patterns is presented to them, the brain activity shows a "double-exposure" effect—a pastiche of surrealistic phantoms and grotesques.

In a few cases we have been able to probe with the Toposcope some of the deeper levels of the brain, when surgeons have had to remove the upper part of the brain of a patient who has suffered some serious brain injury or disease. As we should expect from theory, the activity from the deep brain is simpler, more urgent, more evanescent than that from the upper regions. Most important of all, there is almost no trace of "memory" or persistence of a stimulated pattern when the upper crust of the brain is missing.

With the united efforts of the many laboratories now mobilized for these studies we can plan our campaign for investigation of the living brain with more confidence than ever before. No doubt, in a few years, both our machines and our notions will seem as crude and incoherent as Berger's first articles did a generation ago.

BIBLIOGRAPHY

READERS interested in further reading on the topics covered in this book may find the list below helpful. It is *not* a bibliography of source material. The books chosen are for the most part addressed to the general reader; they include also some of the more accessible text-books and survey volumes. The list is by no means exhaustive. Nor does it embrace the full range of interest of this book, since much of the work reported here is not yet represented in the pages of any other book. (The date given in italics under each chapter title is the date of its original publication in SCIENTIFIC AMERICAN.)

THE ORIGIN OF LIFE
August 1954

What Is Life? Erwin Schrödinger. Cambridge University Press, 1944.
The Origin of Life. A. I. Oparin. Dover Publications, Inc., 1953.
Time's Arrow and Evolution. Harold F. Blum. Princeton University Press, 1951.

PHOTOSYNTHESIS
August 1948

Photosynthesis and Related Processes. Eugene I. Rabinowitch. Inter-science Publishers, Inc., 1945. Vol. I.
Photosynthesis and Related Processes. Eugene I. Rabinowitch. Inter-Science Publishers, Inc., 1951. Vol. II, Part 1.

NITROGEN FIXATION
March 1953

"Evidence for a Nitrogenase System in Rhodospirillum Rubrum." M. D. Kamen and H. Gest in *Science*, Vol. 109, No. 560; 1949.
"Fixation of Isotopic Nitrogen by Clostridium." E. D. Rosenblum and P. W. Wilson in *Journal of Bacteriology*, Vol. 57, No. 413; 1949.

PROTEINS
June 1950

Proteins and Life. M. V. Tracey. The Pilot Press, Ltd., 1948.

THE STRUCTURE OF PROTEINS
July 1954

Chemistry and Biology of Proteins. Felix Haurowitz. Academic Press Inc., 1950.

THE INSULIN MOLECULE
May 1955

"The Amino-Acid Sequence in the Glycyl Chain of Insulin." F. Sanger and E. O. P. Thompson in The Biochemical Journal, Vol. 53, No. 3, pages 353–374; February, 1953.
"The Chemistry of Insulin." F. Sanger in Annual Reports on the Chemical Society, Vol. 45, pages 283–292; 1949.
"The Principles of Chromatography." A. J. P. Martin in Endeavour, Vol. 6, No. 21, pages 21–28; January, 1947.

THE CHEMISTRY OF HEREDITY
February 1953

"Some Aspects of the Cell Nucleus." A. E. Mirsky in Genetics in the 20th Century. The Macmillan Company, 1951.

THE STRUCTURE OF THE HEREDITARY MATERIAL
October 1954

The Biochemistry of the Nucleic Acids. J. N. Davidson. Methuen & Co., Ltd., 1954.

THE REPRODUCTION OF VIRUSES
May 1953

Virus as Organism. Frank M. Burnet. Harvard University Press, 1945.
General Virology. S. E. Luria. John Wiley & Sons, Inc., 1953.

RICKETTSIAE
January 1955

The Etiology and Pathology of Typhus. S. Burt Wolbach, John L. Todd and Francis W. Palfrey. S. B. Wolbach, Harvard Medical School, 1922.

Rats, Lice and History. Hans Zinsser. Little, Brown and Company, 1935.

Viral and Rickettsial Diseases of Man. Edited by Thomas M. Rivers. J. B. Lippincott Company, 1948.

THE GENES OF MEN AND MOLDS
September 1948

The Principles of Heredity, Third Edition. Laurence H. Snyder. D. C. Heath, 1946.

ENZYMES
December 1948

Crystalline Enzymes. John H. Northrop, Moses Kunitz and Roger M. Herriott. Columbia University Press, 1948.

Dynamic Aspects of Biochemistry. Ernest Baldwin. The Macmillan Company, 1948.

THE METABOLISM OF FATS
January 1954

Enzymes and Enzyme Systems—Their State in Nature. Edited by John T. Edsall. Harvard University Press, 1951.

CELL DIVISION
August 1953

The Cell in Development and Heredity. Edmund B. Wilson. The Macmillan Company, 1925.

Mitosis. Franz Schrader. Columbia University Press, 1944.

The Mitotic Cycle. Arthur Hughes. Academic Press Inc., 1952.

CELL DIFFERENTIATION
September 1953

Chemical Embryology. Jean Brachet. Interscience Publishers, Inc., 1950.

MUSCLE RESEARCH
June 1949

Chemistry of Muscular Contraction. Albert Szent-Györgyi. Academic Press Inc., 1951.

NERVE IMPULSE
November 1952

The Mechanism of Nervous Action. Edgar D. Adrian. University of Pennsylvania Press, 1932.

Electrical Signs of Nervous Activity. Joseph Erlanger and Herbert S. Gasser. University of Pennsylvania Press, 1937.

Chemical Wave and Transmission in Nerve. Archibald V. Hill. Cambridge University Press, 1932.

THE ELECTRICAL ACTIVITY OF THE BRAIN
June 1954

The Living Brain. W. Grey Walter. W. W. Norton & Company, Inc., 1953.